Horizons

Health 3
Building Blocks for Health

Teacher's Guide

Organizer / Writer
Gene Ezell

Major Contributors
Thea Beebe, Janna Brasser, Jesslyn DeBoer, Connie Gergolas

Supervising Editor
Hazel Timmer

Executive Editor
Alan Christopherson

Design and Layout
Leann Kruger

Alpha Omega Publications, Inc. • Rock Rapids, IA

Horizons Health 3 Teacher's Guide

The framework for this curriculum was provided by:
CHRISTIAN SCHOOLS INTERNATIONAL
3350 East Paris Ave. SE
Grand Rapids, Michigan 49512-3054

Printed in the United States of America

ISBN 978-0-7403-1496-4

CONTENTS

ACKNOWLEDGMENTS

In the summer of 1989, a new health curriculum for Christian schools was planned. That fall a survey of teachers was conducted in grades K-6. The survey indicated that health was becoming an increasingly significant component of the elementary school curriculum. The survey also revealed that Christian school teachers were eager to have materials containing a clear biblical perspective.

Dr. Gene Ezell, a professor of health education at the University of Tennessee at Chattanooga, developed a content outline and scope and sequence for the *Horizons Health* series. He also was the first author of materials for teacher guides.

Many other individuals helped in the preparation of teacher guides for grades 3–6. The materials were reviewed and field tested in several schools during the 1991-92 academic year. Also providing input, critiques, and suggestions were Nan Van Klaveren and Pat Knoester. Wendy Blankespoor helped to develop the list of resources for units and lessons.

The publications program was directed by Gordon L. Bordewyk. The supervising editor for *Horizons Health* was Hazel Timmer. Judy Bandstra oversaw production of the materials, and Cheryl Strikwerda Randall created the illustrations.

Role of the Christian School in Health Education

The primary responsibility for educating children belongs to parents. But in the Christian community parents do not have that responsibility alone—church and school also participate in the task of education. The church nurtures the faith of its young members, leading them to understand the implications of faith for their lives. The Christian school teaches children and young people about God's world, equipping them for lives of service. Deriving its authority to educate from the parents who send their children to the school, the Christian school supports and augments instruction provided in the home by teaching all curriculum subjects from a biblical perspective.

One curriculum subject is properly health education. Historically this subject has had low priority in curriculum planning; however, among educators today there is a growing awareness of the importance of health education in a balanced curriculum. Educators are recognizing that in order to promote the well-rounded development of children, the school must give sufficient attention to the healthful living of children as individuals and as members of families and communities. A sequential and comprehensive health education curriculum, such as the *Horizons Health* series, provides the Christian school with the opportunity to deal with basic life issues from a Christian perspective in a consistent way.

The serious health problems facing the contemporary world—the threat of HIV/AIDS, the widespread use of recreational drugs, the prevalence of teenage pregnancy, the easy access to abortion—underscore the need for a sound, Christian program of health education. More than ever before students need current, accurate information and clear direction on healthful living. Today's health crises dramatically highlight the obligation of home, church, and school to work together to bring the lordship of Christ to bear on the health education of the community's children.

General Christian Perspective

A Christian perspective on health education begins with the Bible's account of who we are and why we are here. The Bible tells us that we have been created by God in his image. We have been created male and female. We have been created to live in harmony with God, with each other, and with the rest of creation. And we have been assigned the task of caring for God's world.

The Bible has more to tell us. It tells us that because of sin our relationship with God is broken; because of sin we no longer clearly reflect God's image. We live at odds with God and with one another. We don't take care of the created world the way God intended. Even when we try our hardest, we often end up doing the evil we don't want to do (Romans 7:19). And physical death is inevitable.

But that's not the end of our story. In Christ, God has broken the cycle of sin and death. In Christ, God is making us whole. In Christ, God is restoring our relationship to him and to one another. In Christ, we are able to experience the beginning of new life—eternal life— and the hope of a new heaven and earth. We look forward to complete renewal and restoration.

It is this story of redemption history that provides the underlying perspective on health education in the Christian school. When we talk about family life, sexuality, physical fitness, death and dying, and other health topics, it is always in the context of this story.

Christian Perspective and Health Education

Christians believe that God created each human being as an organic unity. The Genesis 2 account of creation says that the Lord God formed man from the dust, breathed into him the breath of life, "and the man became a living being" (verse 7). The Bible does refer to various aspects of the person—such as the mind, flesh, soul, spirit, or heart—but the stress is on the unity of the whole being. The various aspects of a person—the intellectual, emotional, social, spiritual, and physical—are interdependent. In the New Testament the apostle Paul, writing to Corinthian Christians, supports this point of view. Some Corinthians, influenced by their pagan culture, apparently believed that gluttony, drunkenness, or promiscuous sexual activity did not affect their "spiritual" life. Paul counters by strongly denouncing this attitude (1 Corinthians 6: 12-19).

What is the significance of this Christian view of the person for education? It means that health education cannot be treated as incidental to the curriculum. Rather, it must be an integral part of the curriculum at every level. Physical fitness, nutrition, personal health, emotional health, the functioning of body systems—all strands of the health curriculum— affect the whole child. We must recognize that since healthy living affects us in our totality, health education plays a solid role in developing children and equipping them to serve God in the world.

• •

God has given human beings the task of caring for creation. This task includes being caretakers of ourselves. The *Horizons Health* series helps students fulfill their God-given responsibility in several ways. It teaches them about proper personal and dietary health and encourages them to make good choices in these areas. For example, students learn about the different nutritional value in various foods, how family backgrounds and lifestyles influence eating patterns, and the importance of cleanliness in handling and consuming foods.

The series also teaches students about personal safety, helping them to handle emergencies and to take precautions to avoid injury and harm. Another strand of *Horizons Health* deals with body systems, and students come to understand how they are "fearfully and wonderfully made." Still another strand deals with disease. In this area students learn, for example, about the defenses which God has provided for our bodies, and how each person can help prevent the spread of disease. The strand of emotional and mental health leads students to develop an honest and healthy self-image concept and to deal with feelings in wholesome ways. Finally, a curriculum strand dealing with substance use and abuse acquaints students with the risks associated with tobacco, alcohol, and drugs.

The Christian view of a person's responsibility to care for himself or herself in order to honor God runs counter to the prevailing view in North American culture. Our culture says that what we do with our body is an individual matter. Sports and fitness are often used for self-glorification, elevating the body to a higher status than it warrants. At the same time, abuse of the body through addiction, inattention to nutrition, or lack of exercise is also common. In a culture such as this, spelling out how we honor God with healthful living and nurturing Christian attitudes toward ourselves and others are crucial for the Christian community.

• •

The Christian's view of death and dying also differs from the view prevalent in society. Christians recognize disease and death as part of sin's effects on creation. Physical death is inevitable, but for those who have new life in Christ, death is not the last word. However, even though Christ has removed death's ultimate sting, death is still the Christian's enemy (1 Corinthians 15: 26, 55).

One strand of the *Horizons Health* series helps students view death and dying from this Christian perspective. In ways appropriate to the developmental levels of the students, the curriculum deals honestly with topics such as fear of death, inevitability of death, and ways Christians cope with death and dying.

• •

Christians are called to reflect God's love in all their relationships. The social health strand of the health curriculum assists students to develop mature Christian attitudes towards others. They also learn interpersonal skills necessary for getting along with others. Thus students are lead to become contributing members of their communities. To answer our deepest needs, God created us to live in relationship with others.

Christians believe that marriage and family are part of a loving God's design for the human race. God, reflecting on his creation, decided that it was not good for Adam to be alone: "I will make a suitable helper for him" (Genesis 2:18). So God established marriage—and by extension, the family—as a cornerstone of creation. As part of God's creation, marriage was very good. The Bible has such a high view of marriage that it uses marriage as a symbol of the relationship of Christ and the Church.

But marriage and family have not escaped the effects of sin. Sin's results are loneliness, alienation, the breaking of family relationships, and the collapse of marriages. In North American society, these effects of sin are also clearly evident. In fact, for some, marriage and the family simply seem outdated institutions that are no longer useful. And pursuing a course of self-fulfillment is held up by many as the highest goal of life.

Christians believe that in Jesus Christ there is healing for brokenness and power to restore family relationships. He calls us to a life of service and responsibility in the family. And although our efforts are imperfect and our homes are not free of trouble, by God's grace family life can be a source of comfort and joy.

The family life strand of the *Horizons Health* series leads students to appreciate the blessings of family life and to assume responsibilities of family membership. Working through family topics—such as resolving conflicts, the importance of basing family life on God's law, knowing how sexuality affects life, and caring for sexuality in a way pleasing to God—helps students to establish basic Christian life patterns, patterns that will have a far-reaching effect on their lives.

• •

In summary, the *Horizons Health* curriculum seeks to teach Christian students how the lordship of Christ results in healthful living. For only as students acknowledge their accountability to God and form their lives according to his Word are they able to become all their Creator wants them to become and live lives of thankfulness and service.

OVERVIEW

1. What is Horizons Health?

Horizons Health is a comprehensive health education curriculum for grades K-8. The series addresses the mental, emotional, social, and spiritual aspects of health as well as the physical. It helps students take responsibility for their health as individuals and as members of families and communities. It gives them opportunity to develop basic life skills—such as communicating, decision making, and resolving conflicts—in order to prepare them to meet the challenges of daily living. Its Christian perspective leads students to recognize that a healthy lifestyle is a lifestyle of obedience to God.

2. How is the curriculum organized?

Horizons Health is a flexible curriculum, organized into independent units. The units can be taught in any order, depending on your curriculum needs. Each unit focuses primarily on one or two main strands of the curriculum, with lesser strands integrated where appropriate. These are the eleven strands, which are addressed at each grade level:

Emotional/Mental Health   Nutrition
Social Health/Interpersonal Skills   Disease Prevention
Family Life/Human Sexuality   Safety and First Aid
Growth and Development   Substance Use and Abuse
Personal Health   Consumer Health
Community Health

The scope and sequence chart shows the topics covered in each strand at this grade level and at the other grade levels of the series.

3. Do concepts covered in health education overlap with those covered in other content areas?

Because this is a comprehensive health program rather than a single-topic program, overlap unavoidably occurs in certain content areas. Health education, for example, teaches students about how their bodies work and how substance use and abuse, physical fitness, and nutrition can effect body structures and functions; however, structure and function of body systems may currently be taught in science. Schools may wish to integrate areas that overlap.

4. What is the personal safety component of Horizons Health?

At grades K-2 the safety unit includes a lesson on stranger education. In addition, at each level from kindergarten through grade 8 there is one lesson in the safety unit on preventing sexual abuse. In age-appropriate ways, each level deals with differentiating appropriate and inappropriate touch, developing self-protection skills, and identifying sources of help in case of abuse.

Since personal safety is a sensitive area, schools should inform parents about the content of these lessons. Clear communication not only creates trust within the community but also ensures that parents will support and reinforce personal safety concepts taught at school.

Before teaching lessons on personal safety, schools should also develop and adopt a protocol for dealing with suspected or reported abuse. Contact the provincial or state department responsible for child protective services to obtain information and copies of relevant laws. Schools interested in obtaining samples of school policy statements on child welfare that include a protocol for dealing with abuse should contact organizations like the the Society of Christian Schools in British Columbia, 7600 Glover Road, Langley, British Columbia V2Y 1Y1.

5. *What is the sex education component of Horizons Health?*
Sex education is placed within the broader context of family life and human sexuality, one of the strands of the curriculum. Thus at every level *Horizons Health* deals with concepts relating to human sexuality. The grade 5 unit "Growing and Changing" deals specifically with the onset of puberty and the changes it brings.

6. *Is HIV/AIDS education included in the health program?*
HIV/AIDS education is integrated into the program as part of the disease prevention strand. At levels K-2 there are no HIV/AIDS-specific lessons; however, the broader health issues and concepts addressed at these levels—preventing communicable disease, the relationship between personal choices and health, and our God-given responsibility to honor and care for our body—establish the foundation for understanding HIV/AIDS-specific concepts at higher grades. At levels 3-6 students learn about AIDS and HIV in age-appropriate ways. Grade 5 material has a lesson on sexually transmitted diseases, including HIV/AIDS.

7. *How can schools best implement a comprehensive health education?*
Planning a strategy to implement the program is crucial for the curriculum to be effective. Three main areas to address are these: keeping parents informed and involved, assisting teachers with resources and training in specialized areas, and providing a school environment that supports the program.

First, parents need to be informed and involved. Because some topics covered in health are controversial, good communication is particularly important. Meeting with parents at the beginning of the year to discuss the content and goals of health education and sending letters home to inform parents about what students are learning and doing in *Horizons Health* (particularly in advance of lessons dealing with sensitive issues) are good basic strategies. Involving parents strengthens the program as health concepts learned at school are reinforced at home.

Second, schools need to provide teachers with resources and training. Many health education curricula have compulsory teacher-training sessions because of the special challenges a comprehensive health education program presents. Some health topics have traditionally not been part of the school curriculum in a formal way, and few teachers have had courses in health education. Thus teachers need opportunities through workshops or in-service training to become comfortable in dealing with sensitive areas such as sexual abuse and substance abuse. In addition, they need resources to support the curriculum and to keep current on health issues. Local or provincial/state agencies and volunteer agencies (for example, the American/Canadian Red Cross or American/Canadian Lung Association) are sources of valuable assistance and offer a wealth of resources. In some cases, inviting experts into the classroom may be advisable.

Third, the total school environment should support the health curriculum and reinforce classroom lessons. Students learn in the classroom about eating snacks that are nutritious and "tooth smart," but does the school ask students to take part in an annual candy sale to raise money for the school? Does the school library contain current materials about a wide variety of wellness issues? What does the climate of the school teach about interpersonal relationships, about living in community? Does the school community model what a Christian community should be? Health education cannot end when students step out of the classroom. Schools need to consider what kind of messages the total environment is sending.

USING HORIZONS HEALTH

The curriculum consists of independent units that can be taught in any order. This flexible design makes it possible for you to choose segments that meet your curriculum needs and your time schedule. The unit summaries found at the beginning of each unit give a quick overview of the unit and help you decide which units or lessons to use.

There are approximately 50 lessons at each of the levels. With a time schedule of a 30- to 40-minute session for each lesson, *Horizons Health* requires daily sessions for 12 to 14 weeks (or 17-19 weeks teaching three sessions per week and 25-27 weeks teaching two sessions per week). An interdisciplinary program, health lends itself to integration with other subjects, such as Bible, language arts, music, art, science, and social studies. Suggestions for integration are included throughout the curriculum.

Horizons Health provides a carefully planned and comprehensive framework for teaching health education. It is meant to furnish guidelines and suggestions; it is not meant to prescribe each step of each lesson. You are the one to mold and adapt the material and translate it to fit your students and your community.

Teacher's Guide Format, 3–6

The units begin with an overview that includes the following components:

- A *Unit Summary* gives an "at-a-glance" list of lessons.
- *Goals* for the unit are outlined.
- The *Background* provides Christian perspective and/or helpful unit information.
- *Vocabulary* lists words students need to know to understand unit health concepts.
- *Unit Resources* offers suggestions of titles of organizations, books, kits, or audiovisuals helpful as teacher or student resources to support the unit as a whole.
- *Lesson Resources* suggests materials for specific lessons. Most of these resources are listed again in the lesson.

The lessons follow this format:
- *Preparation/Materials* lists what things are needed for the lesson and describes necessary preparations.
- *Objectives* for the lesson are outlined.
- *Background* appears in selected lessons providing specific information on health issues, alerting teachers to sensitive lesson topics, or providing Christian perspective.
- The *Lesson* offers a step-by-step outline. Each lesson ends with a suggestion for closing, providing an opportunity for reflection, self-awareness, summary, or evaluation.
- *Related Activities* presents additional suggestions for student activities, expanding or extending the lesson.

Masters for Teacher Visuals are located in the back of the Teacher's Guide.

Resources

Multimedia resources can significantly increase the impact of the health curriculum, and numerous suggestions for resources have been included. Few health education resources, however, are written from a Christian perspective. Careful screening is necessary before using resources in the classroom. In some cases, you may decide to use selected sections or perhaps to use the materials but add a critical evaluation.

The listings provide suggestions for resources, but keep in mind that the health field changes rapidly. So although we have included resources that were once available, you will need to re-examine and look online for sources to keep the curriculum up-to-date.

Many community and national volunteer health organizations offer educational materials in their special areas. These materials, which include kits, songs, multimedia presentations, lesson plans, activities, posters, student booklets, or brochures for parents, are often available at minimal cost. Many of the materials produced by these organizations are listed in the Unit or Lesson Resources. A list of national health organizations is included at the end of the Introduction. Because new materials are constantly being produced, contacting these health organizations periodically will help you to tap an ongoing source of valuable resources.

HEALTH EDUCATION RESOURCES

SHAPE America
> https://www.shapeamerica.org/
>> Free digital Health curriculum resources.

Canadian Association for Health, Physical Education, Recreation, and Dance (CAHPERD)
> http://www.cahperd.ca/
>> National organization committed to promoting health and fitness through a wide variety of programs and publications.

Substance Abuse and Mental Health Services Administration
> http://www.samhsa.gov/

National Family Partnership
> http://nfp.org/

Office of Disease Prevention and Health Promotion (ODPHP)
> https://health.gov/
> https://www.healthypeople.gov/
> https://healthfinder.gov/
>> The Office of Disease Prevention and Health Promotion (ODPHP) plays a vital role in keeping the nation healthy. They manage the three websites listed.

Parents Against Drugs (PAD)
> https://parentactionondrugs.org/
>> Offers current information about drug abuse and a drug awareness.

National Institute on Drug Abuse
> https://www.drugabuse.gov/
>> Their mission is to advance science on the causes and consequences of drug use and addiction and to apply that knowledge to improve individual and public health.

U.S. Department of Health and Human Services
> U.S. Public Health Service
> Centers for Disease Control and Prevention, CDC
> Adolescent and School Health
> https://www.cdc.gov/healthyyouth/
> 1-800-CDC-INFO (800-232-4636)
>> Offers resource suggestions and updated information about HIV/AIDS.

SCOPE AND SEQUENCE

	Growth and Development	Disease Prevention	Substance Use/Abuse
K	• growth awareness • five senses and corresponding body parts • primary/secondary teeth	• germs and disease • preventing spread of germs • effect of smoke on lungs	• defining medicine • rule: only adults give medicine • consulting adult before using any unknown substance • choosing a smoke-free environment
1	• review of five senses • naming external body parts • joints • four main organs: brain, heart, stomach, lungs • interrelationship of body parts • growth predictions • primary/secondary teeth	• defining communicable/noncommunicable disease • preventing spread of germs • immunizations • health checkups • effect of smoking on lungs	• differentiating drugs and medicines • symbols for hazardous substances • identifying some drugs
2	• growth awareness • introduction to body systems • function and interdependence of senses • function and basic structure of eyes and ears • visual/hearing impairments	• disease symptoms • defining bacteria and viruses • how germs enter body • effects of nicotine, alcohol, and caffeine on body • identifying eye problems	• identifying common drugs: alcohol, tobacco, and caffeine • products containing caffeine • effect of caffeine on body • how nicotine enters the body • how alcohol affects physical reactions • differentiating prescription and over-the-counter drugs • reasons for using medicine
3	• overview of body systems: skin, muscular, skeletal, digestive, respiratory, circulatory, nervous, excretory (main parts and interrelationships) • growth and development problems (special populations)	• communicable and chronic diseases • AIDS transmission through blood and hypodermic needles • immunizations, proper food storage, and cleanliness as ways to control disease	• defining terms • proper use vs. misuse of substances • influence of advertising on use of over-the-counter medicines • dosages • labels for information • tolerance and addiction • harmful effects of tobacco, smoking
4	• miracle of life • hereditary factors • structure and function of blood • the immune system • hair, skin, and nails • structure and function of teeth • digestive system: parts of, process of digestion • cells/tissues/organs/systems • functions and kinds of cells	• care of skin • diseases of digestive system • lack of nutrients and disease • alcoholism • long term/short term effects of smoking • review HIV transmission through blood, needles	• review of terms: drugs, medicines, substance, prescription, OTC • side effects of medications • avoiding misuse of OTCs • harmful effects of tobacco, alcohol, marijuana, cocaine • defining alcoholism • refusal skills
5	• respiratory system • variations in growth rates • endocrine system • physical, emotional, and social changes of puberty • reproductive system	• main classes of pathogens • chain of infection • some common communicable diseases • preventing respiratory diseases • sexually transmitted diseases, including characteristics, transmission, and prevention of HIV infection	• review of terminology • demonstrating effect of smoking on lungs • refusal skills
6	• fetal development • stages of life • processes by which cells receive nutrients and oxygen: diffusion, filtration, osmosis • review of main body systems, main parts and functions • hereditary and environmental factors • impairments	• preventing cardiovascular disease • risk factors of cardiovascular disease • diseases of muscular, skeletal, and nervous systems • hereditary and environmental factors in disease • alcoholism and cirrhosis • anorexia and bulimia • AIDS/HIV	• chemical dependency and its effects • steroids • results of substance use • societal pressure to use substances • resisting alcohol advertising • strategies for resisting pressure
7/8	• characteristics of stages of life • review of interdependence of body systems • changes of puberty • review of reproductive system • impairments • identifying learning styles	• biblical view of disease • lifestyle choices and disease • eating disorders • suntanning • sexually transmitted diseases, including HIV/AIDS • review reducing risk of communicable and acquired diseases • understanding reality of health problems	• alcohol, tobacco, drug abuse (student research) • decision-making and refusal skills

	Nutrition	Emotional/Mental Health	Social Health/Interpersonal Skills
K	• food for energy and growing • plant and animal food sources • eating a variety of foods	• created unique • differences and similarities • main feelings • situations and feelings • responding to others' feelings	• minding manners • manners and feelings • listening to each other • ways to share • cooperating
1	• food and body energy • five food groups • eating from all food groups • eating healthy snacks • diet and tooth health	• created unique • alike and different • naming and exploring feelings • body language • dealing with feelings • ways to deal with anger • developing empathy	• purpose of good manners • practicing good manners • active listening steps • sharing • practicing cooperation
2	• five food groups • limiting extras • daily serving requirements • balanced eating • cleanliness and food handling • eating breakfast • smart snacks for teeth	• identifying individual gifts/interests • blessing others with our gifts • review of main feelings • identifying a variety of feelings • feelings and actions • communicating feelings • developing empathy • saying no and feelings	• communicating with others • developing social skills/manners • showing appreciation • helping others • active listening • selfish/unselfish attitudes • importance of cooperating
3	• classifying foods • combination foods • define nutrients needed for growth, maintenance, repair of body • limited nutritional value of some foods • healthy snacks • diet and tooth decay	• self-awareness and acceptance • appreciating diversity • identifying and expressing feelings • emotions and body feelings • how feelings affect thoughts and actions • dealing with specific emotions: fear, hurt, anger, being left out • humor and feelings	• developing friendships • factors that affect friendships • kinds of friendships • showing kindness toward others • laughing with, not at • active listening • resolving conflicts
4	• six major classes of nutrients: fats, carbohydrates, water, minerals, vitamins, protein • function of nutrients • serving size • lack of nutrients and disease • good food, good times	• self-knowledge and knowledge of God • being saints and sinners • individual differences as part of God's plan • using gifts to serve • how others affect self-concept • showing appreciation for others • handling and expressing feelings • avoiding self-putdowns • making decisions	• belonging to groups other than family • showing respect for others • accepting differences • communication skills • working out problems in interpersonal relationships
5	• review of main nutrients and their sources • vitamins, minerals, and their functions • function of water • individual nutrition requirements • nutrition deficiencies and health • influences on eating patterns	• growing up • identifying individual strengths • range of feelings • developing feelings vocabulary • ways of dealing with emotions • expressing feelings without blaming • overall wellness and emotions • dealing with anger in healthy ways	• wise ways in relationships (Proverbs) • forgiveness and maintaining friendships • respecting others • resolving conflicts • social skills • cooperative skills
6	• criteria for proper food selection • diet analysis • nutrients: carbohydrates, proteins, fats • reducing salt and sugar • results of unbalanced diet • eating disorders	• new life in Christ • patterns of life: inherited and acquired characteristics • handling ups and downs of feelings • interaction of feelings, thoughts, and actions • identifying and managing stress • recognizing influences • decision making and peer influence	• identifying social support network • factors that build up or break down relationships • erecting barriers: prejudice, discrimination, labeling • communication: basic elements, verbal/nonverbal, active listening • deciding to care about others
7/8	• proper nutrition and dieting	• identifying self as God's image bearer and God's child • being made new in Christ • self-talk and self-confidence • discovering, accepting, and developing gifts • using gifts to serve God/community • influence of media on self-concept • decision-making values/strategies • setting goals • developing study skills • being assertive • recognizing and expressing feelings	• biblical view of community • types of love • living in community • dealing with internal/peer pressure • using peer pressure positively • friendship • dealing with conflict • communication

	Family Life/Human Sexuality	Personal Health	Community Health
K	• families—part of God's plan • similarities/differences among families • gender differences • feelings and family • our families and God's family • dealing with death	• good health choices • dressing to stay healthy • exercise and rest • cleanliness and health • care of teeth: brushing and checkups	• health helpers • smoke in environment
1	• living things reproduce • families—part of God's plan • kinds of families • contributing to family life • family changes • death and Christian hope • Christian families in context of God's family	• making healthy choices • staying fit • eating from all food groups • tooth care: plaque, brushing, check-ups, diet • grooming and health	• defining pollution • causes of air pollution • health helpers • immunizations
2	• families provide basic needs • human sexuality, a gift of God • exploring gender differences/similarities • resolving conflicts • family rules • new beginnings and forgiveness • family heritage and traditions • dealing with death	• good health habits • keeping fit and active • avoiding too much TV • getting enough sleep • eating a balanced diet • eating healthy snacks and breakfast • review of good grooming habits • tooth care: brushing, flossing, snacks	• noise pollution
3	• God's law of love as the basis of family living • depending on family members • communicating in families • living patterns and culture • life cycle and the family • sexual identity, an integral part of a person • dealing with death	• benefits of fitness • being physically fit; flexibility, endurance, strength • good posture • oral hygiene • eating healthy foods • benefits of sleep	• health agencies • role of community workers in safety
4	• institution of marriage/family • responsibility and family life • family and the wider community • communicating • death and dying	• components of personal health • building physical fitness • importance of cleanliness • posture • sleep and rest	• effect of contaminated food, water, air
5	• wellness in family relationships • family's impact on members' development • foundation of marriage • changes during puberty • authority/freedom in family life • coping with change in family life • death and dying	• concept of wellness • review of personal health practices • keeping a healthy balance • inventory of health habits • fitness and overall health • exercise and respiratory endurance	• air pollution • water pollution and health • community health resources
6	• stages of life/development • courtship, marriage intimacy • beginning of human life • fetal development and birth process • being a Christian family • societal pressures and family life • changes in adolescence and family life • death/dying	• healthy lifestyle • benefits/components of fitness • weight, strength, posture, obesity, losing healthfully • care of skin, eyes, and ears • importance of sleep/rest • oral hygiene • personal cleanliness/disease prevention • setting health goals	• community problems caused by substance abuse • treatment for alcoholism • community health resources
7/8	• family life • sexuality vs. sex • biblical view of sexuality • myths of sex and sexuality • changes in puberty • chastity and abstinence • healthy male-female relationships • sexual abuse	• healthy lifestyle choices • influence of fashion on ideas of beauty • dieting and health • physical fitness and overall wellness • review components of health fitness • review personal hygiene concepts	• community resources for getting help for substance abuse/other health problems

	Consumer Health	Safety/First Aid
K		• rules and safety • poison safety • medicine and safety • traffic safety • strangers and safety • fire safety: basic rules • emergency phoning • appropriate/inappropriate touch
1	• health checkups	• medicine safety • poison safety: basic rules and household poisons • safety and strangers • review of fire safety • car passenger safety • dealing with emergencies • appropriate/inappropriate touch
2	• aid for visual and hearing impaired	• care of eyes and ears • review of stranger education • intro. to bike safety • review of fire safety • home escape plan • seatbelts • emergency phoning • preventing sexual abuse: appropriate/inappropriate/confusing touch • good and bad secrets
3	• influence of ads on use of substances • labels as a source of information • reasons for using common health products	• risk-taking • bicycle safety • water safety • electrical appliances • preventing sexual abuse: appropriate/inappropriate touch, trickery, self-protection, sources of help • action plan for an emergency • first aid: scrapes, nosebleeds, burns, blisters
4		• accidents—emotional, decisional factors • review of basic safety rules • playground safety • bicycle safety • fire safety, flame hazards • home alone • preventing sexual abuse: definition, touch continuum, self-protection
5	• advertising and food choices	• taking responsibility for safety of self and others • basic emergency first aid • rescue breathing • preventing sexual abuse: defining sexual abuse, saying no assertively, sources of help
6	• getting correct health care	• taking responsibility for safety of self and others • safety in extreme hot or cold weather • safety and natural disasters • review of basic safety rules • home hazard check • defining/preventing sexual abuse: • self-protection, sources of help
7/8	• evaluating advertisements • media sales techniques	• review of basic safety and first aid • responding in emergencies • preventing sexual abuse • identifying and practicing self-protection skills

Looking at Your Body

Goals

- Students will be introduced to these body systems: skin, muscular, skeletal, respiratory, digestive, circulatory, excretory, and nervous systems.
- Students will develop an appreciation for the complexity of the human body and recognize God as their Creator.
- Students will develop sensitivity to people with impairments.

Background

In *Beyond Doubt* (Christian Reformed Board of Publications, 1980), Cornelius Plantinga tells an anecdote about Whittaker Chambers, a dedicated atheist. One day when Chambers was watching his child as she sat in her high chair, "he found himself staring with fascination at his daughter's tiny, intricate ear. It seemed to him a marvel. Only a *planner* could have planned that ear." This experience "set Chambers on the road to belief."

The human body is truly amazing. And it's very smart. In fact, it's brilliant. It performs to a large extent "on its own." The heart beats, lungs breathe, stomach digests, kidneys purify—all without our even thinking about it. When we study the human body—its parts, processes, growth, and development, we cannot help but wonder at the complexity of its design. But like Chambers, our study should lead us to marvel not only at the body, but at the God who created it.

God has given us life, and that life is mysteriously and inextricably linked to a body so complex that we will never completely understand it. Our fitting response is awe and wonder and praise to God, the Creator. "I will praise you," said the psalmist, "because I am fearfully and wonderfully made; your works are wonderful, I know that full well" (Psalm 139:14).

Vocabulary

Integrate the following suggested vocabulary:

body systems

skin	epidermis	dermis	pores
sweat glands	fatty layer	nerve endings	

muscular system

biceps	sprain	skeletal muscles	triceps
strain	voluntary muscles	involuntary muscles	

skeletal system

skeleton	skull	simple fracture	compound fracture

circulatory system

veins	arteries	oxygen	blood vessels
capillaries	carbon dioxide		

respiratory system

lungs	alveoli	trachea	bronchial tube
diaphragm			

digestive system

saliva	esophagus	liver	salivary glands
pancreas	villi	small intestine	large intestine

nervous system

spinal cord	nerves

excretory system

kidneys	bladder
disability	

Unit Resources (Search online for similar resources if these are no longer available)

Cole, Joanna. *The Magic School Bus Inside the Human Body.* New York/Toronto: Scholastic, 1989.

Anatomy Home Learning. Innerbody Research.
 Interactive human anatomy systems, multi-media and text. Suitable for a variety of ages.

The Human Body Project. Scholastic.
 Unit plan with three lesson plans and 8 reproducibles. Grades 3-5.

Suzuki, David, with Barbara Hehner. *Looking at the Body.* Toronto: Stoddart, 1987; New York: John Wiley, 1991.
 Suzuki takes a lively look at the how main organs and systems of the body function

Lesson Resources (Search online for similar resources if these are no longer available)

Lesson 3
"Be a Fingerprint Detective." Scholastic.
 https://www.scholastic.com/parents/school-success/learning-toolkit-blog/be-fingerprint-detective.html. Activity for ages 4-10.

Lesson 4 and 5
Showers, Paul. *You Can't Make a Move Without Your Muscles.* New York: Crowell, 1982.

"Anatomy Home Learning." Innerbody Research. https://www.innerbody.com/htm/body.html.
 The skeletal and muscular part of this page are relevant to these lesson.

Lesson 6
"The Truth About Your Heart." National Geographic Kids.
 https://kids.nationalgeographic.com/explore/science/the-truth-about-your-heart/.

Lesson 7 and Lesson 8
Information about the lungs and digestive system, written for kids, can be found through
 https://kids.britannica.com/ and https://kidshealth.org/.

Lesson 10
"Brain Games." National Geographic Kids.
 https://kids.nationalgeographic.com/videos/brain-games/#/689772099755.

"Your Amazing Brain." National Geographic Kids.
 https://kids.nationalgeographic.com/explore/science/your-amazing-brain/.

Lesson 11
See Unit Resources.

Lesson 12
Contact local branches of national organizations that deal with disability concerns to obtain
 educational materials.

"DISABILITY AWARENESS CLASS ACTIVITY LESSON PLANS." HIE Help Center, 2008.
 https://hiehelpcenter.org/disability-awareness-class-lessons/.
 Lesson plans that teach children to be inclusive.

Disabilities Awareness Packet. Possibilities, Inc., 2006. https://www.dvusd.org/.
 Printable packet with information and activities, covering a wide range of disabilities.

LESSON 1: BUILDING GOOD HEALTH

Preparation/Materials
- Student Activity
- Student books
- Optional: chart paper

Objectives
- Students will identify the various aspects of the whole person: physical, emotional/mental, social, and spiritual.
- Students will recognize that being healthy involves the whole person.

- Students will decide as stewards of God's creation to make healthy choices.

Background
This lesson introduces the topic of health and the whole person. Physical, emotional/mental, social, and spiritual health are inextricably interwoven. The spiritual is central. Being at peace with God brings wholeness and harmony.

• •

Lesson

1. On a large sheet of chart paper or on the board, write the words WHO WE ARE. Challenge the class to give suggestions about the topic. As students offer suggestions, group the ideas into one of four major areas—physical, emotional, social, and spiritual. Expect many ideas related to the physical, especially at first. If necessary, encourage students to branch off into other areas. As the list under each group grows, students should begin to see relationships between the items in each area. Help them discover how to label each area. Explain or elicit from students what each category covers: physical— what we see on the outside, what a doctor would see on the inside; emotional—what we feel and think on the inside and how we show what we feel and think; social—how we act and react with others; spiritual— who we are in God's eyes and how we relate to God.

As you discuss, lead students to appreciate the close interrelationship of these four categories. How does our brain control our feelings? What is the relationship between feelings and how we get along with others? Or between our physical condition (tiredness, illness, etc.), our feelings, and how we get along with others? How is our caring about others a reflection of our relationship with God? Consider drawing lines on the chart to show the interrelationships.

Social caring friendly fun-loving	**Physical** nose mouth can bleed skin covering body
Emotional surprised angry sad happy hurt scared	**Spiritual** love God prayerful

WHO WE ARE

2. **Student book.** Distribute the student books and give students the opportunity to page through them. Then read and discuss the introduction, which stresses how healthy living affects the whole person—physical, emotional, social, and spiritual.

    Discuss the role that students themselves have in being healthy. Note that in their studies of health students will get accurate information about how their bodies work, and they will also learn skills (for example, how to give first aid or avoid accidents, etc.) related to health; however, they also need to make healthy choices. Incorporate "Think It Over" questions in the discussion.

    1. *Answers will vary.*
    2. *Answers will vary; lead students to see that good eating and living habits help promote their growth and development.*

3. **Student activity.** Single students may color and complete the puzzle activity in the workbook. For a classroom setting, divide students into groups to complete the puzzle activity that works with and demonstrates the interconnectedness of the four categories introduced in Step 1.

    Each group needs a puzzle sheet—with one side showing four concentric circles and the other side blank. Students begin by cutting out the pieces of the outer "physical" ring. Direct them to write a word or phrase on the back of each piece that describes that part of who a person is. Follow the same procedure with the other three rings. When the puzzle is completely cut apart, have groups shuffle the pieces and reassemble the puzzle.

    If time allows, groups can exchange puzzles and work each other's puzzles.

    As students work on the puzzles, comment on how the four different aspects of a person are engaged during the activity!

4. Conclude by reading Psalm 139:1–16. Talk with the class about the meaning of the verses: God knows every part of our being; God created us and put us together. What is the fitting response? Thanking and praising God and taking responsibility for living in a healthy way.

• •

Related Activity

*   Integrate with language arts and have students write in a journal about "who I am" in each of the four categories: who I am physically, who I am emotionally/mentally, who I am socially, and who I am spiritually. Consider taking four days to complete this, writing on one topic each day. An alternate option: students can make a five-page booklet in which they reflect on "who they are."

WHO I AM	**Physical**	**Emotional**	**Social**	**Spiritual**
	This is what I look like:	I feel happy when_____	When I play with a friend we like to	I feel close to God when _____
	hair_____	I feel angry when_____	_____	_____
	eyes_____	I am scared when_____	_____	
	height_____			

LESSON 2: LOOKING AT YOUR BODY SYSTEMS

Preparation/Materials
- Small machine such as a radio-controlled vehicle
- Student books
- Optional: clock, toy, or other small machine that is broken beyond repair

Objectives
- Students will begin to discover how the different body systems work together.
- Students will develop appreciation for their amazing bodies.

Background

This lesson begins with students examining a working machine of some kind. Give students the opportunity to figure out which button controls what function of the machine. Electricity probably provides the energy source. Evaluate the machine as carefully as possible—include parts that can't be seen (How do the wheels turn? What's happening inside to make the machine work?).

Then move on to the "body machine." As the students move different parts of the body, they should stop and think of what parts are involved. The object is to lead them to begin to see how all the body systems work together and make us able to do all the things we do.

As you end the overview of the body, be amazed with the class at how wonderfully we are created. No machine can work the way we do! Lead students to understand that we are much more than machines.

- -

Lesson

1. Show students a small machine such as a radio-controlled car and demonstrate how it works.

2. Ask students to discuss all of the things that they see the machine doing. Next ask each student to write a sentence or two telling what they think is happening inside the machine. Ask volunteers to read what they've written. (If you have a broken machine, this is a good time to show its "insides." Are students surprised by what they see? Why or why not?)

3. Have student partners work together to begin thinking about how their "body machine" works. Tell one of each pair to jump up and down three times while partners observe. Ask some observers to describe what they *saw* the body doing. Then direct those who observed the first time to complete an action such as shaking their heads from side to side two times or moving their arms in big circles. Again ask partners to describe what they *saw.*

4. Direct students to write on their papers what they think was going on *inside* the body during what they observed.

Some students may have difficulty getting started with their descriptions. After giving time for students to come up with ideas, you may wish to provide a few clues by writing these words on the board:

muscles   lungs   bones   brain   blood   skin

Have volunteers share their responses. Students most likely will come up with some interesting answers. Accept all responses; answers need not be considered right or wrong.

Explain that in their health studies the class will be talking and learning about what goes on inside the body. They may want to rethink their guesses.

5. **Student book.** Take time to look at the pictures of the various systems that students will be covering. Make this a time of discovery rather than a lecture on how parts fit together. Elicit comments from class. Consider using these questions in your discussion:
   - "What do we see on the outside of the body?" (The skin.)
   - "If we took off all the skin, what would we see?" (Muscles.)
   - "What are the muscles attached to?" (Bones.)
   - "What's under and protected by the bones?" (Parts/organs of different body systems that help us breathe, get rid of waste material, digest food, pump and carry blood to all parts of the body, and send messages to control the whole body.)

LESSON 3: LOOKING AT THE OUTSIDE— YOUR SKIN

Preparation/Materials
- Magnifying lens, one for each child or pair of children
- For activity in Step 2:
  water and cotton balls
  optional: rubbing alcohol
- Student books
- Optional: chart paper

Objectives
- Students will identify the basic structure of skin.
- Students will learn about three main jobs of the skin.

Background
The skin is composed of three main layers: the epidermis, the dermis, and the subcuta-neous or fatty layer. The skin suit of each person is truly amazing.

What are some things skin does for us? Skin covers us and keeps in our fluids. It works with the sun to manufacture Vitamin D. It protects us from the sun and from invaders, germs trying to get inside. It is one way we get rid of body waste (sweat contains extra water, salt, and a little urea). Skin also helps to control our body temperature. When it's hot, skin sweats; the evaporating sweat cools us off. When it's cold, blood vessels in the skin constrict to keep blood warmer and away from the surface of the skin. Of course, special nerve endings, called sensors, are also in our skin. They provide the sense of touch. In this lesson students will discuss three functions of the skin: protection, temperature control, and sense of touch.

Lesson
1. Use the magnifying lenses to take a close look at the skin and get students thinking about the structure of skin. Distribute the lenses and, if necessary, instruct students on how to use them correctly. (Tell students to place the lens on the object they are studying and slowly move the lens up until the object is in focus. If they raise the lens too far, the object will be blurred. They do not need to put their eyes close to the lens.) What does skin look like? Have students share their observations. Record the observations on the board or on chart paper.

2. Do an activity to demonstrate one of the functions of the skin—controlling body temperature through perspiration.

   Begin by having students to recall how they feel right after a swim on a hot day. Ask: "Why does your body feel so cool?" Demonstrate how the skin controls body temperature with a simple water and/or rubbing alcohol experiment.

   Choose two students to stand facing the class. Have them close their eyes and extend both hands. Wet their hands with water or alcohol (alcohol cools more quickly because it evaporates more quickly). What do students notice? (Hands should feel cooler. If students have difficulty with the descriptions, ask if their hands feel wet, dry, hot, cool, etc.). If time allows, give the whole class the opportunity to try the activity with partners or in small groups.

Discuss how sweating can help control body temperature. Ask students when and why we sweat. Draw comparisons to the water/alcohol activity and what happens to the body after a swim. Lead students to the conclusion that perspiration cools down the body when it becomes too hot. Our skin is our built-in air conditioner!

3. **Student book.** Ask students to read "Looking at the Outside—Your Skin" to discover more jobs that the skin does.

Ask students to identify some amazing things about skin (fits perfectly; grows with us; stretches and folds as necessary so that we can move). Have volunteers give their opinions on where the thickest and thinnest skin is on the body (thickest is on soles of the feet—about ⅛ inch; thinnest is in the eyelid—$\frac{1}{500}$ of an inch).

Discuss the three functions of the skin described in the book: protecting the body, controlling body temperature (tie in with Step 2 activity), and keeping us aware of what is going on around us through our sense of touch.

Examine the drawing of skin with the class. Have students name the layers of the skin and notice the pores, sweat glands, and nerve endings. Where are these located in the skin?

Use the "Think It Over" questions to further explore the topic of skin.

1. *Protect, control body temperature, sense of touch; other not mentioned in text is to keep fluids in body.*
2. *Helps to protect the body—especially the abdominal organs that do not have protection of bones.*
3. *Answers will vary.*

• •

Related Activities

1. Make skin prints to increase appreciation for the complexity of skin. Have students rub with a soft pencil on a sheet of paper. Next, direct them to roll part of their skin (fingertip, palm, back of hand, wrist) in the rubbing to pick up some black lead. Then with a piece of clear sticky tape have students pick up the impression on the skin and then carefully press it onto a clean sheet of white paper. (Students may have to practice a few times.) How many types of skin prints can students produce? What are some different kinds of "designs" in skin?

2. Investigate fingerprints. Why are fingerprints useful? A good resource is *Fingerprinting,* one volume in the Great Explorations in Math and Science Series (GEMS). (See Lesson Resources.)

3. Highlight another skin fact—skin on fingers and toes has fewer nerve endings to detect heat and cold than skin on other parts of the body. Demonstrate with a simple experiment: have students place their right wrist and their left forefinger in a bowl of hot or very cold water. Does the wrist or the finger feel the heat or cold the most?

LESSON 4: LOOKING INSIDE— YOUR MUSCLES

Preparation/Materials
- Student Activities 1 and 2
- Student book
- Optional: at least one piece of elastic about 18 inches long

Objectives
- Students will be able to explain the function of muscles.
- Students will begin to identify skeletal muscle groups.
- Students will identify two types of common injuries to muscles.

Background

The body has more than 600 major muscles. The two main types of muscles are skeletal muscles and smooth muscles. The third type of muscle is cardiac muscle, a type that combines characteristics of both skeletal and smooth muscles and is found only in the heart.

More than 400 of the body's muscles are skeletal muscles, muscles that hold the bones of the skeleton together and make the body move. A large part of the body's arms, legs, chest, abdomen, neck, and face consist of skeletal muscle. Some of these muscles (the thigh muscles, for example), are strong and big; others are small and relatively weak (the eye muscle, for example).

Skeletal muscles are attached to bones by tough, cord-like tendons and are controlled by nerves, which receive orders from the brain. When a nerve stimulates a muscle, the muscle contracts, or shortens, and pulls on the bone to which it is attached. All body actions are the result of this one body action—pulling. For this reason most skeletal muscles must work as opposing pairs in order to move the body. One muscle of a pair (the flexor) contracts while the other muscle (the extensor) relaxes.

Skeletal muscles are also called voluntary muscles because they usually work under conscious control. With practice, our muscles can "learn" how to ride a bicycle, play a musical instrument, or use a racket to hit a tennis ball.

The second main type of muscles, smooth muscles, control body processes. Called involuntary muscles because they are not under conscious control, smooth muscles are tireless, working steadily to keep on doing things such as sucking in air and pushing food along, and pumping blood (cardiac muscle is also involuntary muscle). Their pattern of movement is rhythmic—contraction followed by relaxation.

Lesson

1. Introduce the lesson with one or more activities that help students discover how muscles work and the location of muscle groups.

   - Ask students to hold one hand, palm up, against the bottom of their desks or tables. With the other hand, have them locate and feel the muscles of the upper arm. As students hold the position, have them exert pressure or try to push up the hand under the desk. Ask: "Which muscle in your arm do you feel tightening/contracting?" (The front upper arm muscle.) Next have students lay a hand on the top of the desk, palm down, and push down on the desk. Again, have them feel action of the muscles while they're pushing. Which muscle contracts now? (Back upper arm muscle.)

- Use a piece of elastic to demonstrate the contracting/relaxing movement of muscles. Have volunteers hold one end of a piece of elastic in their right hand and with their left hold the other end of the elastic at the bend in the right elbow. As they move the lower arm up and down, the class can see how the elastic gets longer and shorter. Explain that when one muscle contracts, the other must relax. (The student book uses the example of the biceps and triceps.)

- Have students work in pairs or groups of three to find groups of muscles necessary for various body movements. Refer to the Student Activity 1 recording sheets. If the class did the first activity under Step 1, begin by filling in the muscle location for the two actions as a class. Then have students do the movements and consider which muscles are involved. After completing the recording sheet, compare students' lists and encourage students to share their discoveries. Did they discover other muscles and movements?

2. **Student book.** Examine the picture of the muscular system. Have students identify where short muscles and long muscles are found in the body.

   Ask students to read the sections in the student book on the muscles. Tell them to pay close attention to the different kinds of muscles described. You may wish to have volunteers read aloud and stop to discuss each section with the class. As you read about how the triceps and biceps work together, have students feel the muscles working, and as you discuss tendons, help them find tendons in the wrist or back of the ankle.

   Discuss ways that muscles can be injured. Give students the opportunity to share some stories about muscle injuries. Consider discussing muscle strain of the lower back caused by lifting objects incorrectly. Demonstrate how to bend legs and use thigh and leg muscles to help the back lift.

   If you are reading and discussing the book as a class, you may wish to use the "Think It Over" questions as you work through the material. If students are reading on their own, you may wish to use the questions for a class discussion or for individual or group written work.

   1. *Muscles that work with bones.*
   2. *Muscles that we control; skeletal muscles are voluntary muscles.*
   3. *Control basic body functions—breathing, digestion, blood circulation, etc.*
   4. *For our protection. What if we forgot to breathe?*
   5. *Answers will vary.*

3. **Student activity.** Refer to Student Activity 2 and have students use words in the word bank to fill in the names of important muscles. Use the student book diagram for reference.

Related Activities

1. Examine the muscle of a whole chicken leg. Peel away the skin so that students can clearly see the meat (muscle). Point out how the muscle is attached to the bone by short white cords, or tendons.

2. Use yarn to give students an idea of the structure of muscle. Have students separate strands of a piece of yarn; explain that muscle is made up of bundles of fibers. Explain that when a voluntary muscle works, not all the fibers contract at once. Although we're not aware of it, fibers take turns working, with some fibers resting while others pull or contract.

3. Use resources list to extend the lesson.

LESSON 5: LOOKING INSIDE—YOUR BONES

Preparation/Materials

- For Step 4 experiment:
  leg bone of a chicken or turkey (clean, with no meat on it)
  vinegar, enough to cover the bone
  jar with lid
- Student books
- Student Activity
- Optional: model of human skeleton

Objective

- Students will identify two functions of bones: protection for soft parts of the body and support for the body.

Background

The human skeleton provides the body with a framework. Each part of the skeleton is marvelously shaped to fit its specific purpose. Its bones provide solid support for the muscles and skin. Bones also protect important organs such as our brain and lungs.

To do their job, bones must be strong and rigid; mineral deposits (a balance of calcium and phosphorus salts) provide this necessary hardness. But bones must also be resilient; their porous construction helps them to resist bumps and blows.

The experiment in Step 4 demonstrates what happens when the minerals in bone are dissolved. If you want to set up a control for this experiment, put another bone in a jar of water and watch what will—or will not— happen. (Note: Because this experiment takes two to three weeks, begin it at the beginning of the unit if you want to observe the results during this lesson. Or you can start the experiment during the lesson and then observe changes each day.)

- -

Lesson

1. Tell students that in the last lesson they took a look under the skin and found muscle. In this lesson they'll see what's under the muscles. Have the class turn to the student book to look at the picture of the human skeleton. If you have a large skeleton model, display it. What's under the muscle? (Bone.)

2. Have students feel some of their bones. Start on the head and feel the skull. Feel around the eye sockets. Press fingers in front of the ears and open and close the jaw. Where is the jawbone?

   Continue exploring body bones by feeling the collarbone and breastbone. Can students count how many ribs they have? Have them reach around and feel the backbone. Why do they think there are so many bones in the back? Then go on to feel bones in the leg and ankle and foot.

3. **Student book.** Consider the question of why we have bones. Ask: "Why do we need a skeleton?" Give students time to reply to this question, and then turn to the student book and read "Your Skeleton" and "All Kinds of Bones." Two functions of bones are

stressed: giving the body support and shape and giving soft parts of the body protection. The human skeleton has 206 bones. Consider using "Think It Over" questions 1–4 as you discuss the functions of the skeleton.

Next discuss the function of joints. Ask: "Why do we need joints?" Then read the section entitled "Joints" and answer "Think It Over" question 5.

1. *Hold body up, give body shape; protect soft parts of body.*
2. *Bones—the skull.*
3. *Check drawing: breastbone, ribs.*
4. *Answers will vary. Consider telling students that at their age the backbone is made up of about 33 separate bones; but as they develop, some of these bones will join—fuse. An adult backbone has only 26 bones.*
5. *Joints allow you to bend and move parts of your body in various directions.*

4. Chicken bone experiment. Do an experiment to show students that calcium and other minerals are what make bones hard. Show students a cleaned chicken bone, either the thigh bone or leg bone, and give them the opportunity to feel how hard the bone is. Put the bone in a jar and *cover* the bone with vinegar (change the vinegar every few days). Ask students to predict what will happen to the bone. Observe the bone each day by taking it out and feeling it. What is happening to the bone? When the bone has become soft and rubbery, ask students to tell what they think calcium and other minerals do for the bone (provide hardness). Note that without hard minerals, the bone is very similar to cartilage.

5. Discuss broken bones. Read about fractures in the student book. Discuss the difference between a compound fracture and a simple fracture. (A simple fracture is a break in the bone; in a compound fracture the broken bone breaks through the skin.) Talk about the importance of keeping the break area still and seeing a doctor promptly. What may happen if bone is not set by a doctor? (Bone will heal, but perhaps not as it should.)

If you have an extra chicken bone, break one so that the students can see what a fracture looks like.

6. **Student activity.** Students can review the main bones of the skeleton by filling in the blanks, using words from the word bank. The student book diagram can be used for reference or checking work.

Related Activities

1. Discuss how our bodies get the calcium nec-
    essary for strong bones. Have students
    research foods that contain calcium.

2. Learn the scientific names of various bones.
    Many children of this age enjoy learning
    these "big" names. Use simple games to
    make the activity fun.
    - Ask students to find, for example, their
      femur—as you point to yours. Move
      quickly through the names of other
      easy-to-find bones such as the sternum,
      mandible, scapula, patella, clavicle,
      humerus, and phalanges.
    - Fill in those three-minute gaps in the
      school day with a Simon-says activity that
      uses the names of bones: "Simon says,
      'Point to your patella...'"

3. Students can refer to the drawing of the
    skeleton in the student book for scientific
    names. You may also wish to make a
    skeleton bulletin-board display and label
    the bones the class is learning.

4. Integrate with language arts by writing sto-
    ries or poems about bones. Starter ideas:
    - The man/woman/child whose bones
      were made of rubber
    - The bone and muscle(s) that didn't get
      along
    - The sad skeleton
    - Help! I broke my clavicle!

5. Tap resources listed at the front of the unit
    to reinforce or extend the lesson: *My Body
    and How it Works* by Q.L. Pearce; *Your Bones
    and Muscles,* a National Geographic film-
    strip; *Looking at the Body* by David Suzuki;
    "The Main Frame," a song from *Slim Good-
    body's Musical Guide to What's Inside.*

LESSON 6: LOOKING INSIDE— YOUR LIFE'S BLOOD

Preparation/Materials

- For examining the underside of the tongue: magnifying lenses
- Optional: mirrors, one for each pair of students
- Tennis balls, at least 5 or 6 (If the class is small, try to have one for each student.)
- Stethoscopes, one for each pair of students (funnels, paper towel tubes, or toilet paper tubes can function as rough stethoscopes.)
- Student visual of the heart
- For dissecting (see Step 6):
  lamb or beef heart
  sharp knife and scissors
- Student books
- Student Activity

Objectives

- Students will be able to explain the basic parts and function of the circulatory system.
- Students will be able to explain the basic structure and function of the heart.
- Students will become familiar with the reasons for different pulse rates and be able to take their pulse during different activities.

Background

This lesson gives students several ways to discover how the heart works. A hands-on approach gets students actively involved in the learning. Several suggestions for activities are included. The lesson will take two to three days if you decide to use all the activities. If classroom time is limited, choose just one or two for the class to complete.

Students are very interested in seeing an actual beef or lamb heart. You can usually order a heart through your grocer. If there is a meat butchering and packing plant in your area, most likely you will be able to obtain a fresh heart at a very reasonable price. If you request it, the butcher can leave the blood vessels (and even the lungs) attached to the heart. Although this activity is rather messy, the interest of the students makes the fuss and mess well worth the effort. If you are squeamish about "blood and guts," you may wish to ask another staff member to take over.

Lesson (2–3 sessions)

Day 1

1. Ask students to name the body parts/systems studied so far: skin, muscular system, and skeletal system. Then ask them to identify the name of the system that includes the blood and the heart. Write the words *circulatory system* on the board. Tell students that they will be doing a number of interesting activities to help them learn about the circulatory system. If you plan to dissect a lamb or beef heart, be sure to let the class know.

2. **Student book.** Read "Looking Inside—Your Life's Blood" to give students an overview of the circulatory system and its work. Pause at appropriate places to look at the diagram of the body's circulatory system and trace the path of blood through the body.

At this level students learn one of the blood's main jobs—delivering oxygen to cells and carrying carbon dioxide from the cells to the lungs. After reading "Heart Facts," ask students to answer the "Think It Over" questions.

1. *Arteries, veins, capillaries.*
2. *Capillaries.*
3. *Oxygen.*
4. *Carbon dioxide.*
5. *Pumps blood around the body.*
6. *You need more oxygen.*
7. *Answers will vary.*

3. Do one or more of the following activities.
   - Have students examine the underside of the tongue to see veins, arteries, and capillaries. If mirrors are available, have students study the underside of their own tongue; otherwise have students work with a partner (a magnifying lens would be helpful).

   - Use the following information to explain what we can see of the circulatory system on the underside of the tongue.
     - Thick blue lines are the veins. Have students recall that veins are the blood vessels carrying blood to the heart. (Usually blood in veins is "dirty," filled with carbon dioxide and a rather blue color; however, veins also carry "clean," or oxygenated blood, from the lungs to the heart.)
     - Thick pink lines are the arteries. What is the work of the arteries? Carrying blood *away* from the heart. (Usually these look red because they are carrying "clean" blood filled with oxygen to parts of the body; however, arteries near the heart do carry "dirty" blood from the right side of the heart to the lungs to get oxygen.)
     - Tiny, very thin lines are the capillaries. Have students recall that capillaries are the tiniest blood vessels. Blood moves slowly through them. The slow movement gives time for oxygen (and digested food) to go from the blood to the body cells and carbon dioxide and other waste materials to pass into the blood. (Capillaries can also be seen by folding back the skin under the eye.)

   - Have students take their pulses. Explain that there are a few places around the body where big arteries lie close to the surface of the skin. By touching them, we can feel the pumping action of the heart as it pushes the blood along through the blood vessels. This is called the pulse. (When we feel the pulse, we're actually feeling the walls of the artery stretching and relaxing.) Note that the easiest places to feel the pulse are in the wrist and neck.

Help each student locate his or her pulse on the inside of the wrist, along the side on which the thumb is. (Some students may find it easier to locate the pulse in the neck.) Have them place two fingers of the right hand on the left pulse to feel the artery's movement. Explain that the number of times the artery pulses in a minute is the pulse rate (or heart rate).

Have students figure out their pulse rate. Time them as they count the beats for 30 seconds. Then have them multiply that figure by two to find their pulse rate.

• To show how movement or exercise affects the flow of blood, ask the class to run in place or do jumping jacks for a minute or two. As soon as the exercise is finished, again have students take the pulse and figure their pulse rate. How many times per minute did their heart beat before the exercise? After the exercise?

Pulse rate table					
	6–12 years		*18–26 years*		*33–57 years*	
Fitness Level	*boys*	*girls*	*men*	*women*	*men*	*women*
Excellent	73–82	81–92	69–75	76–84	63–76	73–86
Good	83–92	93–104	76–83	85–94	77–90	87–100
Average	93–103	105–118	84–92	95–105	91–106	101–116
Fair	104–113	119–130	93–99	106–116	107–120	117–120
Poor	114–123	131–142	100–106	117–127	121–134	131–144

From *Fitness Discovery Activities* by Charles T. Kuntzleman (American Alliance for Health, Physical Education, Recreation and Dance, 1990).

Day 2—The Heart

4. Begin the lesson with an activity that gives the class an idea of the work of the heart. Pass out tennis balls to students and ask them to squeeze the ball for one minute (as you time them). Repeat the activity; this time have them count how many times they squeeze the ball in a minute. Ask them to try to squeeze it 70 times during the minute. (If there aren't enough balls for everyone, have a second group of students do the activity the second time.) Note that it takes about the same amount of force to squeeze the tennis ball as it does to pump blood out of the heart.

5. Study the structure of the heart. Refer to the visual of the heart in the student work-book. Ask the class how they think blood flows in and out of the heart. Give them time to think of various possibilities. Use the visual and the following information (adapted from the American Heart Association's pamphlet *About Your Heart and Your Bloodstream*) to explain how the heart works.

Inside the heart are four rooms, called chambers. A wall of muscle through the middle divides your heart into a left side and a right side. Each side has two chambers—an upper chamber and a lower chamber. The upper part is called the atrium, and the lower part is called the ventricle.

On each side of the heart, blood flows from the upper to the lower chamber. Little valves act as doors between the chambers. The valves open to let blood flow from the upper to the lower chambers. Then the valves snap shut to keep the blood from flowing back again. (If you have an object with a valve—for example, an inflatable toy—show students how the valve works.) The heart valves snapping shut make the noise doctors hear when they listen to the heart. The heart makes a lub-DUB, lub-DUB sound. The top valves make the "lub" sound and the bottom ones make the "DUB" sound. (Tell students that in a few minutes they'll have the opportunity to listen to a heart beat.)

Blood is always filling both sides of your heart. Blood filling the right side of your heart has just finished a trip around your body. It comes into your heart through large veins and flows from the upper to the lower chamber. From there it is pumped out of the heart and into an artery to the lungs.

Blood filling the left side comes from the lungs. It flows through a big vein. It's bright red because it is loaded with oxygen picked up in the lungs. It enters the upper chamber and goes to the lower chamber. Then it is pumped out through a large artery.

This may be a good point at which to briefly review what students learned earlier about the circulatory system. Ask: "Where does the blood in the arteries go?" (Travels to smaller and smaller arteries until it reaches capillaries.) "What does the blood in arteries bring to all the parts (cells) of the body?" (Oxygen.) "What does it pick up?" (Waste products, carbon dioxide.) "Then where does the blood travel?" (Back to the heart, entering on the right side with its bluish, "dirty" blood.)

Stress that the blood always flows in one direction, and the bluish blood and the red blood don't mix. The heart wall separates the fresh blood from the used blood, and valves keep the blood from flowing backward.

6. Give students the opportunity to use stethoscopes to hear a heart beat. Funnels, paper towel or toilet paper tubes, or top sections of plastic bottles will all function as rough stethoscopes. Keep background noise to a minimum, and have students place the stethoscope on a partner's breast bone. The heart lies in the middle of the chest, a little to the left.

   Have students share results. What sound did they hear? Was it hard to hear the heartbeat?

7. Examine a beef or lamb heart.

   Begin by carefully looking at the outside of the heart.
   - Look at its shape.
   - Check for hard, fatty deposits. Discuss how the fat might affect the pumping action of the heart.
   - Try to find the blood vessels that supply the heart itself with blood. Explain that although the heart pumps blood on the inside, the heart muscle itself must also have its own blood supply (to provide food and oxygen). Blood vessels on the outside of the heart deliver what the heart needs in order to work.
   - If the larger blood vessels leading to the heart are still attached, try to trace where they go. If you are not too squeamish, put your finger into one of the blood vessels and perhaps allow the students to feel it.

   Use a sharp knife to cut the heart open. Try to cut carefully into a chamber of the heart so that the class can see the valve connections. The valves look like strings connected to part of the heart. Also look at the thickness of the heart muscle.

8. **Student activity.** Have students use the word bank to label the main parts of the circulatory system. They can use the diagram in the student book for reference.

9. **Closure.** Note that students have learned some important things about their heart and bloodstream. Stress that it took scientists years to find out what the class has learned in a few sessions. Scientists are still studying the heart and blood system and learning new things about it all the time. Reflect on the Master Designer of this amazing body system.

● ●

Related Activities

1. Conduct a class survey of pulse rates. Students can determine the pulse rate of different family members. Students could compare pulse rates and ages, pulse rates of smokers and nonsmokers, and rates of those who exercise regularly and those who don't. Make charts of the results.

2. Raise awareness of how many miles of blood vessels are in the human body by having students compare the mileage with distances on a map. There are 60,000 miles (96,540 kilometers) of blood vessels in the human body. What places are 60,000 miles from their town?

3. Use some of the excellent resources listed or others online to extend or reinforce lesson concepts.

LESSON 7: LOOKING INSIDE— YOUR LIFE'S BREATH

Preparation/Materials
- For checking breathing rates: clock or stopwatch
- Student Activities 1 and 2
- Student books

Objectives
- Students will identify the basic parts of the respiratory system.
- Students will identify the main function of the respiratory system.

Lesson

1. Introduce the respiratory system by asking class members to close their eyes and concentrate on their breathing. Tell them to keep their eyes closed as they answer the following questions. Accept.all answers; the idea is to get them thinking about the respiratory system.
   - "Can you hear yourself breathe?"
   - "Can you hear others around you breathing?"
   - "Are all your breaths the same length?"
   - "Try to estimate how many times you breathe in a minute." (Later in the lesson students will read the answer in the student book: 15–20 times a minute.)
   - "What does it feel like when you take a deep breath?"
   - "What part of your body is moving when you breathe?"
   - "What part or parts of your body takes in the air?" (Air enters through the nose and/or mouth.)
   - "Is there any other way you can take in air?" (No.)
   - "What do you think happens to the air you breathe in?" (Encourage students to explain as much as they know of the respiratory system without comment or correction.)

   Tell students that this lesson will help them learn more about the respiratory system.

2. **Student activity.** Have students test their breathing rates after a few activities such as an active Simon Says routine, a Follow-the-Leader activity that includes skipping and hopping, or a brief time of running in place. Refer to Student Activity 1 in the student workbook. Explain that the class is going to see how different activities affect their breathing. After each activity, students will figure out how many times they breathe in a minute and record it in the space provided. To arrive at the correct figure, they should count the number of breaths they take (the number of times they inhale) in 30 seconds (teacher timed) and then double the number. Remind the class that in order to get reliable results they should try to breathe naturally. Be sure to have them record their breathing rates before the exercise for comparison.

Share the results. Do the numbers vary widely? Are they close to the estimates students made in Step 1? Did being aware of their breathing make it hard to breathe naturally? Are students usually aware of their breathing?

3. **Student books.** Turn to the student book and read "Looking Inside—Your Life's Breath." Study and discuss the diagrams and answer the discussion questions.

   1. *A cold plugs up nose/air passages. Still, it's possible to breathe through the mouth.*
   2. *To take in oxygen and get rid of carbon dioxide.*
   3. *Factory smoke, car exhaust, burning trash, etc.*
   4. *Answers will vary.*

4. **Student activity.** Have students complete Student Activity 2, using the word bank to fill in the blanks and name the main parts of the respiratory system. Students can use the student books for reference and checking.

Related Activities

1. Demonstrate the characteristics of carbon dioxide. Fire needs oxygen to burn (much the same way we need oxygen to "burn" food in our body); carbon dioxide can put out a fire.

   Place a small candle in a container (for example, a peanut butter jar). Light the candle. Then pour carbon dioxide into the jar. The heavy carbon dioxide will fill the jar from the bottom and then put out the candle.

   How do you obtain carbon dioxide for the experiment? One way to make the colorless gas is by mixing vinegar and baking soda. Take a balloon and place its opening over the narrow end of a funnel (you can make a funnel by cutting off the top section of a plastic soda bottle). Turn the funnel over and push a tablespoon of baking soda into the ballon. Carefully remove the balloon from the funnel. Next, pour about ½ cup of vinegar into a small soda bottle. Being careful to keep the soda inside the balloon, stretch the end of the balloon over the mouth of the soda bottle. Hold up the bal-loon, letting the soda fall into the bottle and mix with the vinegar. The balloon will inflate with carbon dioxide. Remove the balloon and pour some of the remaining carbon dioxide over the candle. Another method is to use dry ice, which is frozen carbon dioxide. The gas that comes from the ice will put out the candle.

2. Measure lung capacity by filling a gallon jar with water and turning it upside down in a tub of water. Place a tube from the mouth of the jar of water to the side of the tub. Take a breath and breathe out through the tube. As you exhale, water will be forced out of the gallon jar and the "top" of the jar will now contain air. Measure the amount that the water goes down to find your lung capacity.

3. Conduct a survey of breathing rates. Students can use copies of the student activity recording sheet to test family members. They can again check breathing rates of people of various ages, of smokers and nonsmokers, etc., and chart the results.

4. Compare the respiratory systems of humans to that of fish or other animals. What are the similarities? What are the differences?

5. Extend the lesson by using the resources listed or others found online.

LESSON 8: LOOKING INSIDE— YOUR DIGESTION

Preparation/Materials
- Soda crackers, at least one for each student
- Jar of baby food—corn
- For egg experiment (see Step 4):
  raw egg
  vinegar
  jar
- Optional: provide another raw egg for comparison (store it in the refrigerator during the experiment)
- Student books
- Student Activity
- Apple slices, one per student

Objectives
- Students will be able to identify the major parts of the digestive system.
- Students will be able to explain how food travels through the digestive system.

Background
Food is not really *in* the body until it leaves the food tube and goes into the blood stream to be carried to the various parts of the body. This part of the digestive process takes place in the small intestine. Villi line the small intestine, and with their folds they provide a large surface for food contact. During digestion nutrients are broken down into small particles in order to go through the villi and into the surrounding blood vessels. This is the process of osmosis. The villi are like tiny screens; small food particles (that have been broken down into sugar particles or amino acids, or other nutrients) can get through the opening of the screen, but larger particles cannot.

The experiment with the egg demonstrates this process. Small particles of water can go through the lining of the egg, but the larger protein molecules of the egg white cannot go through. So the eggs get bigger because water is going in.

The cracker-eating activity demonstrates how food is broken down, a process that begins in the mouth. Saliva does more than wet our food. It contains a chemical, an enzyme called amylase, which breaks down starch to its component parts—sugar molecules. Other enzymes further along the digestive system interact with other types of foods to break them down into a form the body can use. Although students will not find it easy to keep the chewed-up cracker in their mouth for any length of time, if they can manage to hold it for about five minutes, they will start to notice that the taste of the cracker is turning sweet as the starch changes to sugar.

• •

Lesson
1. Briefly review the importance of oxygen and how oxygen gets to all parts of the body through the respiratory and circulatory systems. Ask: "What else do we need besides oxygen to stay alive?" (Students may have several suggestions; the one the class is focusing on today is food.) "How do parts of our body get the food they need?" (Accept all responses, and note that the class will get the full answer in today's lesson.)

2. **Student book.** Read and discuss "Looking Inside—Your Digestion" for an overview of the function and structure of the digestive system. As the class reads about the digestive process, refer to the diagram and have students follow the path that food takes in the body. Incorporate the "Think It Over" questions in your discussion.

    1. *In the mouth: teeth, tongue, and saliva work together to prepare food to be swallowed.*
    2. *Squeezes to mix food; adds juices-acids to further break down food. By the time the food leaves the stomach it is a thick liquid.*
    3. *Liver and pancreas.*
    4. *It passes through walls of villi into the bloodstream.*
    5. *Water is removed from wastes, and wastes are gradually moved along until they are pushed out of the body.*
    6. *The large intestine is much shorter and much wider than the small intestine. The small intestine is 21 feet/6.5 m long, and the large intestine is 5 feet/1.5 m long.*

3. Use one or both of these activities to show students the "power" in their saliva.

    • Give each student a soda cracker. Students should chew the cracker and then hold it the mouth—without swallowing—for five minutes. (It's hard not to swallow some of the cracker, but encourage students to do the best they can.) Tell students to pay attention to the taste of the cracker from the time it enters the mouth.

    Ask: "How did the taste of the cracker change?" Students will have noticed that the taste became sweet. Explain that the change was caused by a substance or chemical (an enzyme called amylase, which changes starch into sugar) in their saliva. Saliva not only helps digest food by adding wetness to the food to help the teeth make food into mush, but a chemical in saliva has the job of breaking down starch into sugar. You may wish to explain that other chemicals are added to the food as it goes through the digestive system in order to break food down. (The liver, pancreas, and gallbladder all make chemicals for food breakdown.)

    • Obtain a jar of baby food such as corn. Add a few drops of saliva to the jar. Leave it standing in the classroom overnight. Have students check the corn the next day. The saliva will have broken down the starch into a soupy mixture.

4. Set up an experiment to demonstrate how it is possible for particles that are small enough to pass through the intestinal villi into the blood stream.

    • Place a raw egg in a jar and pour vinegar over the egg. The vinegar should reach about ½ inch above the egg because during the experiment the egg will expand. Cover the jar.

- Observe the egg each day. The shell will gradually dissolve because the vinegar dissolves the calcium in the shell (just as it dissolved the calcium in the chicken bone in a previous lesson), and the egg will become rubbery. But the point of this experiment is the change in the size of the egg. The egg will gradually get bigger. Keep another raw egg at hand to compare size.

- How does the egg get bigger? Explain that the only way for the egg to become bigger is by having something from the vinegar travel into the egg through the membrane. What traveled through? Water (molecules) in the vinegar is made up of small enough particles to get through the membrane. They caused the egg to expand like a balloon that is blown up. Why doesn't egg white travel through the yolk membrane in a similar way? The egg white is made up of large particles (protein molecules); for this reason they are unable to pass through the membrane.

Make the comparison to what happens in the small intestine. In the process of digestion food is broken down to small enough particles to simply pass through the villi into the blood stream. This process is called *osmosis.*

5. **Student activity.** Distribute a slice of apple and refer to the Student Activity sheet in the student workbook. Students should wait for instructions before they eat the apple. Direct the class to imagine that they are traveling with the apple as they eat and digest it. Have them write the story of what happens to the apple on the activity sheet. They should also write the names of the various organs of the digestive system.

• •

Related Activities

1. Help students visualize the length of the intestines. Adult intestines are about 26 feet (8 meters) long. Give students yarn or string and have them measure and cut a piece as long as the intestines. Or cut the piece of yarn or string before class, roll it in a ball; then have the students unroll it.

2. If possible, show a video or film about the digestive system. Video clips can be found online (one suggested video is through ted.ed.com).

LESSON 9: WASTE TREATMENT PLANTS

Preparation/Materials
- For playing kidney game:
  Game Boards 1 and 2, one for each individual or for a group of 2–4 students—colored paper clips as movers, one per student
  game cards, one of each kind of waste (a total of three) per student
  dice, one die per student group
- Student books
- Materials for making additional games as desired

Objectives
- Students will identify the wastes the body produces.
- Students will be introduced to the different ways in which the body gets rid of its waste materials.

Background
The body has four main systems for waste removal: (1) the lungs, which exhale carbon dioxide; (2) the skin, which gets rid of water, salts, and a little urea; (3) the large intestine, which expels worn-out cells, dead bacteria, and undigested food; and (4) the kidneys, which process water, acids, nitrogen wastes, and yellow pigments. Most people are aware that the last two, the intestine and the kidneys get rid of wastes, but many people don't think of the skin and the lungs as waste removers. However, they are very important in the process of removing wastes.

This lesson includes a game to help students visualize the way the kidneys work. If you and your students enjoy games, your class could create their own games (based on student book information) about the other three waste treatment plants of the body. A sketch of a game about waste removal and the large intestine is included in the lesson.

Suggestions for preparing the kidney game: the students may color both game boards in their student workbooks, then remove and mount the game boards on strong paper or cardboard. For long wear, cover them with clear contact paper or have them laminated. For a classroom setting, prepare one game board for every two to four students.

Lesson
1. Introduce the topic of body waste by asking the class what would happen if we had poison on our food or in our water. Class members probably will respond that poison will make us sick and might make us die. Draw a comparison to what might happen if we didn't get rid of body wastes. If we don't get rid of the wastes, they can become a kind of poison. So the "waste treatment plants" of the body are very important. Although we may feel embarrassed talking about the job of the kidneys and intestines, these parts and functions of the body are important and normal! God has designed these systems in a wonderful way to keep us healthy.

2. **Student book.** Have the class read "Waste Treatment Plants." The material tells students about the four waste treatment plants of the body: skin, lungs, intestines, and kidneys. Students are familiar with the first three, but probably not with the kidneys/urinary system.

As you discuss the urinary system, tie in to the discussion of poison in Step 1. Consider comparing the blood to a river that must be kept clean and free of pollution. The kidneys filter the blood, removing the wastes and changing them to urine. Kidneys also control the level of water and salt in the blood. Without the kidneys, blood would become polluted and kill us, in the same way that pollution in a river can kill off plant and animal life. Study the main parts of the urinary system.

Study the diagrams of skin, digestion, and respiration in previous sections, if necessary, to explain how these systems expel wastes from the body.

3. Play the game about kidneys. The purpose of the game is to help the class become familiar with the way the body gets rid of liquid wastes/purifies the blood.

   Game instructions:
   - To play the game, each group of two to four students needs playing pieces (such as colored paper clips; one per student), a die, game cards, and game boards. (For individual students, both game boards, three waste cards (one of each), a die, a playing piece, and an opponent are needed.)
   - The three main waste materials removed by the kidney are *acids, yellow pigment,* and *nitrogen wastes.* (Read the words on the game cards with the class before playing and explain that these are the three main wastes that the kidney removes.) Each student needs a game card for each of these wastes. Students roll the die and move playing pieces around the board. The object of the game is for students to get rid of their waste cards by the time they reach the end of the board.
   - Players begin on game board #1 at START in a blood vessel leading to the kidney. When they get to the "Wait Here" space, they must place their playing piece in the kidney and stay there until they roll a 3. The 3 allows them to go to game board #2, which is the inside of the kidney, and move three spaces, beginning at the arrow. As the game continues, they move along the blood stream. Each time they land on a space with a star (★), they may discard a waste card. They will need to make choices about their path because if they get to the end of the board without getting rid of their waste cards, they will have to start over. The first person to the end after getting rid of all three of their waste cards is the winner.

4. Consider having the students create a game about waste removal in the large intestine. Have students check in the student book to recall what happens in the large intestine and what products the body gets rid of through the large intestine. (Water is absorbed into the walls of the intestine and the waste becomes solid; worn-out cells, dead bacteria, and undigested food—seeds, celery fibers, skin of fruit,, etc.—are expelled through the anus.) You may wish to work as a class to outline some of these things and then have groups of students design and make their games. An open file folder makes a good game board surface. Cards and playing pieces can be stored in an envelope inside the folder.

Example of a large intestine (colon) game:

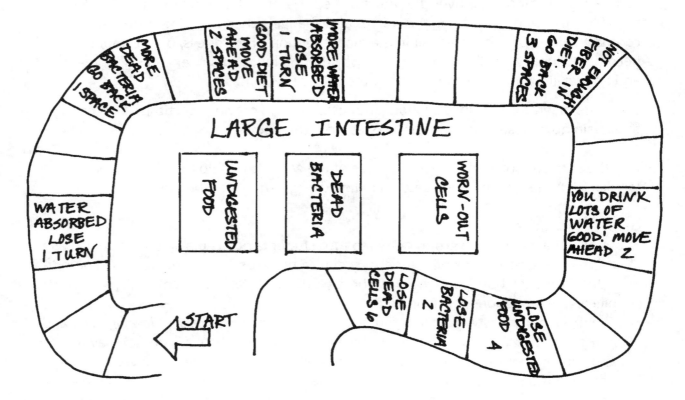

Some students may also to wish to design games for lungs and skin. For example, they could design a lung game in which players get rid of several carbon dioxide cards by moving from alveoli, to bronchial tube, to windpipe (trachea), and on out of the mouth/nose. Players could make the trip from the alveoli for each carbon dioxide card they hold.

Make the game(s) available for students to play during free time.

LESSON 10: CENTRAL CONTROL SYSTEM

Preparation/Materials
- For paper drop reflex game: pieces of paper cut slightly smaller than a $1 bill, one piece for each student or pair of students
- For ruler reflex game: one ruler per pair of students
- Student books
- Student Activity

Objectives
- Students will identify major parts of the nervous system.

- Students will identify the major function of the nervous system.

Background
Some of the activities for this lesson are adapted from *Looking at the Body* by David Suzuki (Wiley, 1991) and from *Blood and Guts* by Linda Allison (Little, Brown, 1976).

• •

Lesson

1. Demonstrate one or more of the following reflex actions to introduce students to the nervous system.
   - Make a sudden loud noise by dropping a book or other object. What is the automatic reaction of those nearby? (Jumping and/or blinking.)
   - Knee jerk. Have one student sit on a desk or table with his or her legs hanging over the side. Tap right below one knee with the side of your hand. (You may need to try a couple of spots before getting a reaction.)
   - "Refix" reflex (actually this is called the vestibulo-ocular reflex). Ask students to hold an index finger about 6 inches in front of their face. First, direct them to move the finger from side to side as fast as they can. Second, direct them to hold the finger still, but to move their head from side to side as fast as they can. When did the finger look blurry? (The first time.) Explain that a part of their brain (the cerebellum) is helping them to focus on what's ahead even when their head moves suddenly. How can this ability help avoid accidents? (For example, even if we hit ruts or bumps when we're biking, we're still able to keep eyes focused on other obstacles ahead of us.)

2. **Student book.** Note that these automatic responses of the body are called reflex actions. What are some reflex actions? List them on the board (jumping, blinking, ducking, arm movements, turning head or body, etc.).

   Ask: "What body system is responsible for these fast reactions?" (The nervous system.) "What are the parts of the nervous system?" Accept all responses and then have students turn to the student book, "Central Control System."

   Study the diagram of the nervous system. Have students point out the brain, spinal cord, and nerves on the diagram.
   Read and discuss the text with the class.

Use the following information for discussion. The nervous system has receivers (eyes, nose, ears, tongue, and skin—the senses) and doers (muscles and glands). In the example given in the book, the ears are the receivers when the telephone rings, and the muscles are the doers. The receivers send the message along nerves to the control center, the brain, and the brain returns the message to the doers. All these messages travel very quickly around the body, similar to the way electricity travels to a light bulb when we turn on a switch. (Turn a light switch on to give students idea of the speed with which the messages travel along the nerves.) It takes scientists with very sophisticated equipment to even measure the speed at which these messages travel.

Incorporate the "Think It Over" questions into your discussion.

1. *Brain, spinal cord, and nerves.*
2. *They carry messages to and from the brain.*
3. *For thinking, remembering, moving, etc.*
4. *Answers will vary.*
5. *Answers will vary.*

3. Do one or more of the following activities to help students understand how the sensory nerves, brain, motor nerves, and muscles work together to control movement.

- Paper catch activity. Give each student or pair of students a piece of paper. Students should stand and hold the paper high above their head, drop it (dropping it on its side will help it flutter as it comes down), and try to catch it. Try some variations: catch with one hand, aim to catch at waist level, have one student drop and another student catch.

  Discuss what is going on as you try to catch something. Your brain must estimate where the object will be and then react so that your hands are at the right place at the right moment. Compare catching the paper to catching a ball: the falling paper moves more slowly, but it is harder to catch than the ball because it is unpredictable and the brain has to readjust its fix and send new signals. Consider how a strong wind can have much the same affect on the movement of a ball and make it harder to catch.

- Ruler catch activity. This activity is a variation on the previous activity. Each pair of students should stand facing each other. Student 1 holds a 12-inch ruler (on the 12-inch end) between thumb and forefinger. Student 2 holds places a thumb and forefinger about 2 inches apart just below the 1-inch end of the ruler. When the first student lets go of the ruler (not before), the other student should try to catch the ruler by closing thumb and forefinger around the ruler. Have students check at which number on the ruler the partner makes the catch. Can they catch faster as they repeat the activity? Is the brain learning something in the process?

- Knee jerk. Consider having student pairs try the knee jerk reflex. After they experiment with the reflex, have them use sound ("Jerk your knee—now!") to get the body to do the same thing. Which response is faster? Explain that a reflex message doesn't have to go as far as the brain to get a response. The spinal cord sends the automatic, involuntary reaction while the message goes on up to the brain.

- Play a well-known memory game. Begin the game by saying a simple sentence such as "I went on a trip, and I took along a book." The second person repeats the sentence and then adds an item ("I went on a trip, and I took along a book and a flashlight."). Each subsequent person repeats the whole list in order and then adds another item. If a person misses an item, he or she drops out of the game. (Those who are out of the game might like to write down the items as they're said.)

  Talk about the game. Did students do specific things to help themselves remember? How did people act as they were trying to remember? (Close their eyes or some similar action? Try to shake a forgotten item out of their brain by going over the whole list again from the beginning?) Why was it easier to remember the first few things on the list? Much about how people remember things is still a mystery.

4. **Student activity.** Have students complete the worksheet to review the main parts of the nervous system.

· ·

Related Activities

1. Do an activity to discover how habits save time and help us avoid unnecessary conscious effort. Direct students to write their full name as many times as they can in one minute in a single column on a sheet of paper. Then in a second column have them see how many times they can write their name backwards in a minute (for example, senoJ yraM). How does habit help with writing? Brainstorm other habits that save time.

2. Find out more about how the brain works. Read books such as *About Your Brain* by Seymour Simon or show the National Geographic filmstrip *Your Brain Helps You*. Students can also make a drawing of the brain and label it main parts.

3. Focus on the receivers of the nervous system, the five senses by adding in additional resource.

LESSON 11: PUTTING IT ALL TOGETHER

Preparation/Materials
- Space to run or jump
- Student Activity

Objective
- Students will become aware of how the various body systems and parts work together.

Background
During this unit students have been looking at separate body systems. This lesson looks at the whole body and stresses interrelationships between the various systems.

• •

Lesson

1. Briefly review the different systems/parts of the body covered in the unit. Note that even though the different systems and parts have their own jobs, the systems work together.

2. Have the class do an activity that gets them thinking about how the systems and parts of the body work together.

   Divide the class into pairs or trios, and assign each group a different kind of exercise: running in place, jumping jacks, imaginary rope jumping, stepping up and down repeatedly from a box or similar object, waist bends, and so on. Tell each group to think about what they've learned in the unit and pay attention to what the body is doing. Ask students to consider questions such as the following:
   - "What parts of the skeleton are working and how?"
   - "What are the muscles doing?"
   - "How is the heart responding?"
   - "How are the lungs working?"
   - "What about the work of the skin?"
   - "What is the nervous system doing? What messages are being sent to the brain?" "What messages is the brain sending to the muscles?"
   - "What about the digestive system? Is it doing anything? How is it contributing?"

   After three minutes of exercising, direct each group of students to write a paragraph about what was going on in their bodies. On the board write a list of words that should appear somewhere in the paragraph, for example, bones (skeleton), muscles, heart, lungs, skin, brain, and nerves. Each group can brainstorm ideas. Members of the groups can take turns writing the sentences that make up the paragraphs. Share and discuss results. Note the contributions of the digestive system and waste treatment plants: without the digestive system breaking down food and distributing it, we wouldn't have the energy to be active; waste treatment plants are keeping body clean on the inside so we are able to be healthy.

3. **Student activity.** Use the worksheet for further review of how the body works. Students can do the worksheet individually, using the student book as a reference. Or consider having students work on the review in groups.

> *Matching: 1 (b), 2 (g), 3 (i), 4 (d), 5 (c), 6 (e), 7 (h), 8 (a), 9 (f), 10 (j)*
> *Fill in the blanks: 1 (bones), 2 (muscles), 3 (nerves), 4 (brain), 5 (heart), 6 (blood vessels),*
> *7 (oxygen), 8 (oxygen)*

Alternative options:

After the exercising, have individual students quickly list as many things they can think of that were going on in the body during the activity. Or work as a whole class to come up with ways in which parts of the body were working together during the exercise activity. Write the list on the board or on chart paper.

Related Activities

1. Students can make up riddles about the parts of the body or body systems. Have them look at the example on page 29 of the student book. Collect the riddles into a class book.

2. As a review, read books or show films about how the body works. Reference the resources list or other sources.

LESSON 12: DEVELOPING AN UNDERSTANDING OF OTHERS

Preparation/Materials

- Meter or yard stick
- Large, long-sleeved shirt with buttons, two or three
- Wheelchair and/or a walker or pictures of them
- Unit Evaluation
- Optional: recording of Joni Erickson Tada

Objectives

- Students will develop sensitivity and compassion for people with special problems or disabilities.

- Students will understand that people with disabilities have unique strengths and needs.

Background

Although this unit has primarily focused on how amazing our bodies are and how its parts work together in a truly wonderful way, we all know that in this broken world bodies don't always work the way they should. People may be born with disabilities. Accidents cause injury and impairments. Diseases affect body parts or systems. Through this lesson help students to understand the difficulties that physical limitations may impose, and help them to respond with sensitivity.

Lesson

1. Remind the class that although the lessons on body systems have focused on the way healthy bodies work, people's bodies don't always work the way they're "supposed to." Invite class members to give examples of different physical problems people might have.

2. Discuss the problems "little people" have. Use a measuring stick to show the height of an "average" adult (about 5'4" to 6'2"). Then measure a height of about 4 feet. Explain that adults who are about this height or shorter usually have a hereditary condition called dwarfism.

   Ask a few children (or, if you wish, the whole class) to get on their knees on the floor. Measure a few of them. Note that some "little people" are only 3' tall.

   Lead the class in brainstorming problems that a person of this size would have during a day at school, or at work, or at home.

3. Have the class consider what it would be like to have a physical impairment that limited or prevented the use of one arm. Ask a few children to put on large, button-up shirts, keeping one arm out of the sleeve. The rest of the class should ask them to do various tasks (for example, get something from a lunch box or write a word on a piece of paper). A note of caution: don't allow this activity to become silly or funny.

   Discuss what difficulties students using one arm encountered. What might cause such a disability? By dealing with a disability what other strengths might a person develop?

4. Show students the wheelchair and walker or pictures of them. What problems would people who need to use these encounter? If you have a wheelchair, have someone sit in it and lead the class on a walk through the school and into the school yard. If not, take a walk with the class and find places that would create problems for someone in a wheelchair or with a walker.

5. Close the lesson with a discussion about how we can show caring and love to others, especially to those with impairments. Use questions such as the following to lead the discussion:
   • "Are people with disabilities very much like you or very different from you?"
   • "What would be wrong with doing everything for a person with a disability?"
   • "How do you react when you see a person with a physical disability on the street or in a store?"
   • "How do you think God wants us to treat people with disabilities?"

   Note that we need to be very thankful to God for healthy bodies and take good care of our bodies. But help students to be aware of the importance of concentrating on what people with impairments can do, rather than on what they can't do. You may wish to use the example of Joni Erickson Tada. Joni cannot move her muscles below her shoulders, but she is able to paint. She has a radio ministry and travels and speaks. If you have a recording of Joni singing, play a segment of it for the class.

6. **Unit evaluation.** Use the worksheets for review and evaluation.

   Fill in the blanks: 1 (support, protect), 2 (pairs), 3 (joint), 4 (veins), 5 (oxygen, carbon dioxide), 6 (mouth), 7 (sweat), 8 (nerves)
   Matching: 1 (c), 2 (e), 3 (b), 4 (a), 5 (d)
   Short essay:
   1. Protects, controls body temperature, provides the sense of touch.
   2. You don't have to think to make the muscles move. They just do.
   3. Your body needs more oxygen because it's doing more work; the heart pumps more oxygen.
   4. The stomach squeezes the food, ads juices and acids, and thins food into a thick liquid.
   5. Answers will vary.

• •

Related Activities

1. Contact local community agencies that represent disability concerns for educational resources and speakers. Many fine programs and speakers are available in most communities.

2. Additional materials can be found in the resource section.

3. Have students write prayers expressing thanks for healthy bodies and/or concern for those with disabilities.

You and Your Feelings

Goals

- Students will develop a healthy self-concept.
- Students will identify a variety of feelings and learn healthy ways to cope with feelings.
- Students will learn and practice skills for getting along with others.
- Students will choose to treat others with respect and love.

Background

Unit 2 focuses on one important area of education—affective education. Christian schools are committed to educating the whole child—the emotions and will as well as the intellect. At the grade 3 level students examine several upsetting feelings in some detail and consider the effect of feelings on what they think and do. Lessons on making friends, showing appreciation, listening to others, and resolving conflicts also deal with the role of emotions in relationships or various situations. All the lessons help children understand more clearly what prompts certain feelings. Students are led to express emotions in healthy ways and how to respond in healthy ways to the emotions of others.

What are healthy ways for Christians to deal with emotions? Mary Vander Goot in her book *Healthy Emotions: Helping Children Grow* (Baker, 1987) cautions against two extremes. On one extreme are Christians who promote the idea that good children will have only "nice" feelings. Much popular Christian literature and art promote this idea by picturing only smiling, sweet children. Vander Goot warns that "if we fall into the habit of thinking that pleasant emotions are good and unpleasant emotions are bad, and if we consequently elect to cover up negative emotions rather than attend to them and grow from them, we lose integrity and become emotionally artificial." Showing sadness, fear, or anger is not un-Christian. However, in reaction to this saccharine approach, other Christians have gone to the opposite extreme, maintaining that children should have the freedom to express whatever they feel. This approach is dangerously irresponsible. For although disturbing emotions should not be stifled or denied, randomly expressing anger with no concern for others or failing to deal with the causes of disturbing emotions is also not healthy.

To deal with emotions in a healthy way we must recognize and express the rich variety of human emotions. But we must also learn to control our emotions, to act on them responsibly. Vander Goot puts it this way: "Although our emotions are woven in with our actions, they are counselors to our actions but not their dictators. Our emotions give us a strong sense of our condition; however, we must make insightful and responsible decisions when we act to alter our condition."

To stay emotionally healthy takes maintenance. Vander Goot singles out three goals to work toward: richness, fit, and control. The first goal, richness, means being able to express a wide variety of feelings. Many people live impoverished emotional lives. Although there are many reasons for this, sometimes family and societal patterns are the cause. Some families, for example, don't allow open expression of appreciation, affection, or perhaps fear; society frowns on men expressing fear or sadness and on women expressing anger. A narrow emotional life has wide implications because it keeps us from understanding the emotions of others and thus affects our relationships with others. Fit, the second goal, has to do with how emotions connect with events. Emotions must be fitting; they need to be appropriate to an event. "A pleasant feeling in the face of a horrid event is false, and despair in the presence of great possibilities is equally false," comments Vander Goot. The goal is to work toward fitting emotions and fitting expressions of emotion. Control, the third goal, requires a purpose in life, something to give our lives direction. Only in the light of that purpose or commitment are we able to assess our emotional life and work toward reflecting that commitment in our emotions. The goal of control is not to stifle emotions, but to follow up on emotions "wisely so that our feelings, our relationships, our actions, and our perceptions move toward greater and greater integrity."

Christ, whose kingly rule includes our emotional life, calls us to be his disciples. By God's grace we can learn to become aware of the meaning of our feelings and to act on them in ways that lead us and our neighbors to emotional health.

Vocabulary

Plan to integrate the following suggested vocabulary:

feelings	emotions	laughter	humor	communicate
eye contact	conflict	problem	solve	active listening
solution				

Unit Resources (Search online for similar resources if these are no longer available)

Grimes, Nikki. *The Poetry Zone.*
> https://www.nikkigrimes.com/.
> Books lists and educator guides focused on poetry and multi-cultural literature.

A list of grade appropriate books about homelessness and poverty can be found by visiting
> https://www.doinggoodtogether.org/bhf-book-lists/picture-books-hunger-poverty-homelessness.

More lesson plans about diversity can be found on teacheringtolerance.org.
> You can search lessons by age group and theme.

Short stories about diversity and acceptance can be found by searching through the Teaching Tolerance "Student Texts" section: https://www.tolerance.org/classroom-resources/texts. Search by age group.

Lesson Resources (Search online for similar resources if these are no longer available)

Lesson 1
Books that support Social-Emotional Learning can be found through
> https://shop.scholastic.com/teachers-ecommerce/teacher/tsohomepage.html.
> Search by grade level and genre.

Howe, James. *I Wish I Were a Butterfly.* New York: Harcourt Brace, 1987.
   In this picture book a wise spider helps a cricket who is unhappy with his ugly appearance realize that he is special in his own way.

Books that support Social-Emotional Learning can be found through
   https://shop.scholastic.com/teachers-ecommerce/teacher/tsohomepage.html.
   Search by grade level and genre.
Mills, Lauren. *The Rag Coat.* New York: Little, Brown, 1991.
   When Minna wears a patchwork coat to school and others make fun of her, she explains the story behind each patch. A book about accepting differences for grades K–4.

"Our Best Selves." Scholastic, in partnership with Yale.
   http://www.scholastic.com/ourbestselves/index.html.
   Lesson plans, videos, and activities are available for various topics related to emotional well-being. K-3

Lessons 2–5
Cleary, Beverly. *Ramona the Pest.* New York: Dell, 1982.

Brinckloe, Julie. *Fireflies!* New York: Macmillan, 1985.
   A boy has a good time catching fireflies but then realizes he must release them or they'll die. Ages 6-8.

Grimes, Nikki. *The Poetry Zone*.
   https://www.nikkigrimes.com/.
   Books lists and educator guides focused on poetry and multi-cultural literature.

Henkes, Kevin. *Chrysanthemum.* New York: Greenwillow, 1991.

_____. *Sheila Rae, the Brave.* New York: Greenwillow, 1989.

Honeycutt, Natalie. *The All New Jonah Twist.* New York: Bradbury, 1986.
   Jonah starts grade 3 determined to prove he is responsible enough to have his own pet. All about the trials of growing up.

McLachlan, Patricia. *Journey.* New York: Doubleday, 1991.

_____. *Sarah, Plain and Tall.* New York: HaperCollins, 1985.

Moss, Marissa. *Regina's Big Mistake.* Boston: Houghton, 1990.
   Regina's feelings about a drawing assignment that goes wrong will be familiar to all children.

Sendak, Maurice. *Where the Wild Things Are.* New York: Harper, 1963.

Stoltz, Mary. *Storm in the Night.* New York: Harper, 1988.
   Thomas and his grandfather sit out a storm together. Although a picture book, the lengthy text will appeal to eight-year-old children. Useful for discussing the emotion of fear.

"Free Social Emotional Learning Activities." Centervention.
   https://www.centervention.com/social-emotional-learning-activities/.
   In this section of the website, there are free lessons, activities, and printables (worksheets) about mindfulness and feelings. Additional books are also listed. Suitable for K-8.

Lesson 7
Giff, Patricia Reilly. *Sunny-Side Up.* New York: Dell Yearling, 1986.

Zimmerman, Alycia. Read-Aloud *Lessons to Foster Friendships.* Scholastic, 2018.
    https://www.scholastic.com/teachers/blog-posts/.
    Simple lesson plan with discussion-based activities. List of suggested books. Grades PreK-5.

Hughes, Shirley. *Moving Molly.* New York: Lothrop, 1988.
    A picture book for ages 5–8 about a preschooler who is looking for new friends.

MacLachlan, Patricia. *The Facts and Fears of Minna Pratt.* New York: Harper, 1988.
    Suggested for ages 9–12, this is the story of Minna's growing friendship with Lucas.

Rylant, Cynthia. *All I See.* New York: Orchard Books, 1988.
    The story of a shy boy's growing friendship with a lakeside artist.

Tusa, Tricia. *Stay Away from the Junkyard!* New York: Macmillan, 1988.
    A jolly tale of a new arrival in Jasper, Texas, who makes friends with a junkyard owner.

Dr. Seuss. *The Sneetches and Other Stories. Random House Books for Young Readers,* 1961.
    Collection of stories about empathy, relationships, and inclusivity.
    Recommended for K-4, but suitable for any age.

Waber, Bernard. *Ira Says Goodbye.* New York: Houghton Mifflin, 1988.

Lesson 8
Clifton, Lucille. *Everett Anderson's Friend.* New York: Holt, 1992.
    This narrative poem is an excellent additional resource for this lesson.

Moss, Jeff. *The Butterfly Jar.* New York: Bantam, 1989.
    This collection of poems includes several that describe different types of friends: "Rhoda,"
    "Laura," and "Rachel."

_____. *The Other Side of the Door.* New York: Bantam, 1991.
    Another collection of poems by one of the original creators of *Sesame Street.* "In the Dark,"
    "The Family Next Door," and "One Special Thing" are on the theme of friendship.

Steig, William. *Brave Irene.* New York: Farrar, Straus, and Giroux, 1988.

Lesson 10
Lewis, Kim. *Emma's Lamb.* New York: Four Winds, 1991.

Lionni, Leo. *Matthew's Dream.* New York: Knopf, 1991.

MacGill-Callahan, Sheila. *And Still the Turtle Watched.* New York: Dial Books, 1991.

Prutzman, Priscilla, and others. *Friendly Classroom for a Small Planet.* Philadelphia: New Society
    Publishers, 1988.

LESSON 1: WHAT IT'S LIKE TO BE ME

Preparation/Materials
- Student books
- For making personal history books (see Step 5):
  Art materials for decorating covers
  Option 1: computer paper, 8–10 sheets per student. (Figure one sheet per year of age plus enough for the cover.) Leave each student's sheets connected for accordion effect. Or use butcher paper, a strip approximately 48 to 60 inches long for each student. (Allow 6 inches for each year of age, plus enough for the cover.)
  Option 2: 17" x 11" sheets of construction paper, one or two sheets for each student (see Step 6, option 2).
  Option 3: long strips of butcher paper, one strip from 48" to about 64" long for each student. (Allow 6 to 8 inches for each year of age.)
- Optional: Make a microphone to help with turn-taking. Paint or cover a paper-towel roll with construction paper and attach (with tape or glue) a ball of yarn to one end.

Objectives
- Students will appreciate the diversity of humankind.
- Students will develop self-awareness and self-acceptance.

Background
The self-esteem movement has been the center of vigorous debate in recent years. Floods of articles, books, and films have been produced on the importance of a positive self-image. Wayne Joosse in *The Christian's Self-Image: Issues and Implications* points out that Christians in particular have climbed onto the self-esteem bandwagon, claiming that movement presents "a popular synthesis of biblical truth and psychological health" and a long-overdue correction to the traditional negative "such a worm as I" view prevalent in many church communities. Other Christians, however, resist the self-esteem movement, protesting that it is a form of pride that ignores the sin in each of us or that it further exemplifies the narcissism of North American culture.

Although clearly Christians must critically evaluate the self-esteem movement, there is little question that how children feel about themselves is extremely important. Educators have found a direct relationship between self-esteem and success in school; health educators have found that children with poor self-concept are more likely to take part in unhealthy and risky behaviors. Teachers are abdicating their responsibility if they ignore the importance of self-esteem. Indeed, teachers along with parents are the ones chiefly responsible for shaping self-image in children.

This lesson provides the framework for creating a classroom climate in which student differences are recognized and accepted.

Lesson (2 sessions)
1. Write the unit title, "Getting Along With Myself and Others," on the board. Briefly explain that this unit will help students to discover things about themselves and to think about some problems that everybody faces sometime or another. Then tell students that in the first lessons they will be thinking about "what it's like to be me."

2. Optional: If circle discussions are new to your class, spend time laying down ground rules. Tell students that during this unit class members will be talking together about common concerns, and it's important to agree on the basic rules for the discussions. Ask students to identify what rules they think are necessary. Work with the class to make up a list. Suggested rules to include: speak one at a time (pass an item such as a "microphone" to help with this rule), listen while others are speaking, respect others' opinions, no put-downs. Write the rules on the board or on a chart for future reference.

3. Introduce the topic of discussion, the uniqueness of each individual, by asking students to look around at the group and notice similarities and differences among those in the group. Give students time to think about the topic before offering their observations. Be sure to enforce the ground rules established in Step 2.

   Student observations will most likely focus on physical similarities/differences (size and shape, hair and eye coloring, gender). Note that all people come in different packages, and each package is unique. Consider tying this in to the previous unit's discussion of handicaps, and help students begin to understand that there are things about ourselves that we can't change and that we have to accept.

   Next, lead the discussion to differences of abilities and talents in the group (some can draw, swim, whistle, run fast, play an instrument, make cookies, or climb trees; others can sing or are learning to play an instrument or to row a boat). Have children mention an ability or talent of their own or of another group member (try to highlight an ability of each child). Ask: "Why do you think God has made us with different abilities?" Bring out that we are to use these abilities to serve others.

   Then have students imagine what the world would be like without such diversity. Perhaps ask them to take a good look at you, close their eyes, and imagine what the class would be like if every person in the class looked just like you—only smaller. Further imagine what would happen if everyone in the world wanted to become a teacher.

   Lead students to appreciate the diversity that our Creator God has built into humankind.

4. **Student book.** Read and discuss "Being You." Enjoy the poem "Me I Am!" with the class. What does the author think is special about each individual? As you discuss the "Think It Over" questions, lead students to appreciate the diversity that our Creator God has built into humankind.

   1. *Answers will vary. Suggested answer: accept yourself. Realize you are different from everyone else and it's okay.*
   2. *Answers will vary. Discuss how knowing God accepts us can help us to accept ourselves.*
   3. *Answers will vary. Suggested ideas: each person praises and serves God in an individual way; since each person has different gifts, people need each other.*

5. Have students make a personal history record—an accordion book, flip-up book, or timeline. Or, if you prefer, choose the alternative option and ask students to describe themselves.

    Introduce the activity by telling students that each person also has a unique story or history. If time permits, give a brief sketch of your life, including when and where you came to Christ and were baptized. Consider making a sample of the activity option you've chosen to show to the class. Use your own life as the subject (although you probably won't want to cover every year). Explain that each student will make a booklet or timeline that tells the story of his or her life. Distribute materials and let students get started on the activity.

    Suggested content: Every option requires students to tell something about each year of their lives. Students can write about important happenings of each year ("moved to Omaha," "baby sister joined the family," "broke my leg," or "learned to ride a tricycle). To have accurate information for early years, students should consult parents. Consider writing a letter similar to the following asking for parents' help.

    Dear Parent:

    Each member of our class is making a ("Story of My Life" booklet/timeline). We need your help. Would you please provide the following information?

    Important events in my life:
    Year 1
        When I was born (date and time)
        Where I was born
        How much I weighed
        Where and when I was (dedicated or first attended church).
    Year 2
    Year 3
    (Continue in this way, providing at least one line for each year of life.)

    Thank you for helping us with this project. We know you'll enjoy our finished projects.

    Read the letter to the students, and explain that their parents will be able to help them with details of their early life that they may have forgotten or never known!

    Suggested format:
    *   *Option 1.* Make an accordion-type booklet, using one page for each year of the child's life. Use computer paper to make an 8 ½" x 11" booklet. Or use long strips of butcher paper, pre-folded (accordion style) into the number of desired pages.

        Have students write, and perhaps illustrate, main happenings for each year of life.

- *Option 2.* Make a flip-up book, using one sheet of 17" by 11" construction paper for each booklet. Cut through the top section on the dotted lines.

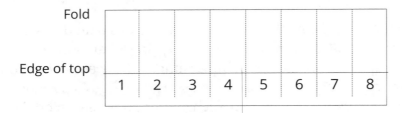

Under each door students can draw pictures and write about that year of their life. For added space, use 2 sheets of 17" x 11" paper. Glue the backs of the finished sections together.

- *Option 3.* Have each students make individual timelines. Use long strips of butcher paper. Consider pre-folding the strips to help to mark yearly divisions. In each section have students write that year's events.

When the books are completed, give students the opportunity to share them with the rest of the class. Take this opportunity to focus on salvation, baptism, and the central importance of the church in the lives of class members. In the ensuing discussion stress that while we were still little babies and didn't know anything about God, God already loved us, promised to be our God, and sent Jesus into the world so that we could become God's children. (Be sensitive to varying beliefs about infant baptism in the homes represented in your class and lead the discussion accordingly.)

Alternative activity:
Have class members write about "what it's like to be me." Have them write a letter describing themselves for someone who doesn't know them at all. Or encourage students to think and write about themselves by assigning the topic "If My Feet Could Talk." The authors of *The Friendly Classroom for a Small Planet* (New Society Publishers, 1988), from which this suggestion is taken, say children find the idea of talking feet to be amusing, and some find it easier to express themselves through this indirect approach.

Spend some time brainstorming or clustering before the writing exercise to help students generate ideas. Lead students to focus on their unique qualities, abilities, interests, and/or histories.

Have volunteers read their descriptions to the class. You may wish to cover authors' names, have students pick compositions at random to read, and then have class members guess whom the composition is about.

6. Summarize/evaluate with questions such as the following:
   - What are some ways in which all members of this class are alike?
   - What are some ways in which we differ?
   - Why you think God created each person unique?

7. Close the lesson with an appropriate song. Suggestions: "You Are Our God; We Are Your People" (*Psalter Hymnal*, #272) and "Children of the Heavenly Father" (*Psalter Hymnal*, #440).

Related Activities

1. Global awareness: Provide pictures of children from around the world. Discuss what all the children have in common and what are some obvious differences.

2. Read books that tie in with the lesson topic. See the resources section.

3. Students can make lists of their favorite things to do, favorite foods, and/or favorite pets. Use the lists to create a "Favorite Things" bulletin board. You may wish to place a photograph or self-portrait of each child next to his or her list.

    Consider creating a graph of classroom favorites in one or more categories. Poll students individually with teacher-made masters (to avoid "copy-cat" syndrome): Then make a bar graph on the board or overhead projector, with each child filling in a square to mark his or her choice.

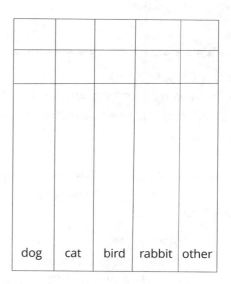

LESSON 2: YOU AND YOUR FEELINGS

Preparation/Materials
- Student books
- Chart paper
- Student Activity
- Write the words of the song "Wherever I Am, God Is" on a transparency or on newsprint.
- Optional: Display pictures of people showing a variety of emotions.
- Optional: overhead projector

Objectives
- Students will develop an increased awareness of feelings.
- Students will recognize that it is normal to experience many different emotions.
- Students will expand vocabulary dealing with feelings.
- Students will discover how feelings are expressed nonverbally.

Background
Although class members will have had class sessions at earlier grade levels on identifying feelings, the lessons are well worth repeating on each elementary school grade level. Children need practice identifying feelings. Many children think they are the only ones who have certain feelings, so talking about feelings and recognizing that others have the same feelings is healthy and helpful. Mary Vander Goot in her book *Healthy Emotions* (Baker, 1987) notes that "one of the first steps to managing emotions is admitting to having them," for "students, who in the process of social comparison become convinced that they are the only ones who have felt the way they do, spend a good deal of their energy hiding their feelings from others and sometimes even from themselves." On the other hand, knowing that others grapple with similar emotions gives students valuable support.

Lesson (2 sessions)

1. Tell students that one way people the world over are similar is that all have feelings. Write *feelings* and *emotions* on the board. Explain or elicit from students the meaning of the words.

2. **Student book.** Have students read and discuss the section "All Kinds of Feelings" in the student book. What feelings do the pictures of the children show? Discuss the "Think It Over" questions.

   1. *They tell the "temperature" of your feelings.*
   2. *They tell you a lot about yourself; they tell you what's important to you. Consider expanding on the answer and leading children to understand how feelings add color and interest to life.*
   3. *Jesus knows how we feel; Jesus understands us.*

3. Brainstorm a list of feelings, writing student suggestions on a piece of chart paper. You may wish to begin by having students recall the four main feelings taught at earlier grade levels—happy, sad, afraid, and angry—and write those on the top of the chart.

Then have students name as many different kinds of feelings as they can that fit under each of the four main categories. Write feelings that don't fit well under these main categories under an "Other" heading.

If students have trouble thinking of words, consider exploring different ways a person might feel when he or she is happy (excited, joyful, friendly, cheerful, thankful), sad (down, hurt, ashamed, sorry, disappointed), afraid (nervous, anxious, jumpy, upset), or angry (grumpy, mean, jealous, frustrated).

4. Go over the list of feelings, and have students think of actions or situations that might evoke each feeling.

5. **Student activity.** Divide the class into pairs, and have each pair plan and give a role-play of an event/situation that evokes one of the feelings. Give each group the description of a situation to act out. (If your class is large, you may need to create and write out more situations than the Student Activity provides.) Individual students may cut apart the role-plays and place them into a bowl. The student may select a role-play and act it out with a parent or partner.

During this activity students should discover or review ways in which we communicate our feelings. After each pair gives its role-play, have the rest of the class identify the feeling or feelings. How did players communicate how they felt? Lead students to identify facial expression, body language (gestures, posture, way of walking or moving), and tone of voice as basic ways we show feelings.

6. **Circle discussion.** Start the discussion by explaining that we are created in God's image, and our ability to feel is part of that image-bearing. Assure students that all feelings are a part of being human. Make the point that God has made human beings with the ability to have many, many different feelings. Continue the discussion with questions such as the following:
   - "Would everyone have the same feelings about a situation?" Refer to one of the role-plays, and lead students to see that reactions of individuals to the same situation may vary. Help them to recognize that the feeling comes from within the individual and that there is not one automatic response to a situation.
   - "Can we always tell how people feel from looking at them or from listening to them?" The point here is to realize that we can misread body language. Someone may not be sad—just tired. Besides, some people may not show how they really feel. If we're not sure, we'd better ask.
   - "Can you think of a time when you had more than one feeling at one time?" If students can't think of an example, give a personal example. Explain that often we can have a combination of feelings that are usually part of the same main feeling (feeling friendly and cheerful—both happy feelings; feeling down and ashamed—both sad feelings).
   - "Which feelings on the list do you like having and why? Which do you dislike having and why? What feelings do people often pretend they don't have? Why?"

- "What is a good way to deal with angry feelings?" Discuss healthy strategies for dealing with anger. Note that anger is a normal feeling, and it's not wrong. Everyone gets angry sometimes. But people are responsible for what they do when they're angry. Stress the importance of slowing down and stopping to think before acting. It's not okay to hurt somebody because you're angry. Calling names or blaming doesn't help either. But it's fine to tell the person that you're angry and try to straighten out the problem.

  Note: Angry feelings are dealt with in Lesson 10 in connection with conflict. You may wish to touch lightly on the topic here or wait until lesson 10 to discuss anger. In addition, the next unit has material on using "I messages" rather than "you messages."

- "Do you think God knows and cares about how you feel?" Lead students to realize the comfort of knowing that God understands us and loves us—even when we are unlovable.

7. Consider starting a unit writing project, a private booklet about feelings. Provide a few starter sentences such as the following:
   - I feel happy when...
   - I feel sad when...
   - I feel angry when...

   Students can write about a feeling on each page of the booklet. If time permits, they can add illustrations of the feeling. Assure students that their books will remain private.

   You may wish to expand this personal booklet to include, for example, the writing suggested in Lesson 7 on the topic of friends.

8. Close the lesson by teaching students the song "Wherever I Am, God Is." Discuss the meaning of the lyrics. You may wish to make this song the unit theme song.

● ●

Related Activities

1. Make feeling collages. Provide magazines and catalogs. Have students work in pairs or groups to cover a large sheet of construction paper with cut-out faces depicting a variety of feelings. Discuss the collages, identifying the feelings.

2. Provide pictures of faces showing different feelings. Ask each student to choose a picture and make up a story about why the person feels that way. Students can write their stories and use the pictures as illustra-tions and/or they can record their stories and later listen to them in groups.

3. Global awareness: invite students or staff members of different ethnic backgrounds to tell the class feeling words in other languages and/or ways of communicating non-verbally in other cultures.

4. Use some of the excellent resources available on the lesson topics. See the Lesson Resources listing.

Wherever I Am, God Is

Carey Landry

LESSON 3: FEELING, THINKING, DOING

Preparation/Materials
- Props as desired for teacher pantomime
- On slips of paper or cards, write situations for group activity. Make up one situation for each pair or group. (See Step 3 for suggestions.)

Objectives
- Students will recognize the interaction of body feelings and emotions.
- Students will understand that feelings affect what we think and do.

Background
This lesson makes students aware of how their feelings may affect what they think and do. The next lesson explores in more detail the necessity of stopping and considering before acting when feeling upset.

• •

Lesson

1. **Introduction.** The following paragraphs are not meant to be a script, but are meant to suggest an approach to the lesson.

"Yesterday we made a list of feelings and talked about when we might have those feelings. Most of the feelings we talked about were feelings we had because something others said or did made us happy, sad, or maybe angry. But sometimes feelings are closely connected to our bodies. I'll give you an example. If I've had a good night's sleep and wake up with lots of energy, I may feel cheerful; but if I didn't get enough sleep, I may be grumpy. My body affects my feelings. Can you think of another time your body might affect your feelings?"

"Sometimes, though, things work the other way. Our feelings can affect our bodies. Can you think of an example of feelings affecting a person's body?" (Some examples: being worried about a taking part in a program can keep us from eating much lunch or breakfast or give us butterflies; when we're excited about going on a trip, sometimes we can't sleep; when we're really scared, body muscles tense and the heart pounds; when we're embarrassed, we may blush.)

"Listen to this situation: the teacher calls on Sam several times in a row. Sam is tired and feels grumpy. Sam might think that the teacher is picking on him. How would it help Sam to be aware of what is making him grumpy?" Bring in the tendency and unhelpful attitude of blaming others.

Explain that it's important to know that our feelings affect what we think and do. In this lesson the class will be exploring how our feelings affect what we might think and do.

2. Pantomime a classroom situation. Tell students that you are going to pretend to be a student in grade 3 named Teresa and act out a classroom situation. Students should try to guess what you are thinking and feeling by watching you. Interact with the class, breaking out of character to give hints as necessary.

   Suggestion for pantomiming: Teresa collects art materials and brings them to her desk. She works hard on a drawing. She dislikes the completed drawing and rips it up. Then she quits trying and sits looking glum.

   Lead students to understand Teresa's feelings and how her feelings affected what she thought and did. "How did Teresa feel?" (Frustrated and angry—and maybe dumb—because things didn't go right.) "What did Teresa think?" (That she couldn't do the work.) "What did Teresa do?" (Ripped up the art work and gave up trying.)

   As you discuss the pantomime, make the point that especially when we're upset about something, we shouldn't act too quickly. We should stop and pay attention to what we're feeling and thinking. Talk about the effect of what Teresa did on the situation. Did she improve matters or make them worse? Work with the students to think of better ways to deal with the situation.

3. Divide the class into pairs or groups (assign a recorder and reporter in each group) and distribute a situation card to each group. Students should decide how Teresa or Sam might be feeling (encourage students to use more than one feeling word) and thinking in each situation. Then bring the full group together and have the reporter for each pair or group read the completed card to the rest of the class.

   If appropriate to the situation, have the class suggest what Teresa or Sam might do if he or she acted too quickly. What would be other ways of dealing with the situation? Students might enjoy voting on what they think the best solution is. When appropriate, also discuss that blaming others doesn't help a situation.

   Here are some suggested situations, but making up situations that specifically reflect your class's interests and problems is recommended.

   - Teresa has a brand new baby brother. Everyone makes a big fuss over the baby and brings him presents.

     Teresa feels_____.

     Teresa thinks_____.
   - When Sam arrives at school, he puts his lunch on the steps of the building. A grade 4 student takes a banana out of his lunch and starts eating it.

     Sam feels_____.

     Sam thinks_____.

- Someone at school has a birthday party. Teresa isn't invited.

    Teresa feels_____.

    Teresa thinks_____.
- Sam is part of a group working on a project at school. The two other students in the group talk to each other all the time. They hardly talk to Sam.

    Sam feels_____.

    Sam thinks_____.
- On field day, Teresa and her friend win the three-legged race. They win a prize. Others tell them, "You were great!"

    Teresa feels_____.

    Teresa thinks_____.
- Sam is having trouble doing his seat-work. It's a hard assignment. When the bell rings, he isn't finished.

    Sam feels_____.

    Sam thinks_____.
- Teresa is in charge of feeding the class's pet gerbil. One day she forgets to feed it. The next morning the gerbil is found dead in the cage.

    Teresa feels_____.

    Teresa thinks_____.
- Someone trips Sam. He falls and bumps his head on a desk.

    Sam feels_____.

    Sam thinks_____.

4. **Summarize.** "Today we learned that our feelings can affect our bodies, and our bodies—for example, when we're sick—can affect our feelings. We also talked about how our feelings in certain situations affect what we think and also what we do. When we're really upset, how we feel and think can sometimes make us do things we're sorry for later or things that only make the situation worse. In later lessons we'll talk again about ways to deal with upset feelings."

• •

Related Activity

- Have students work up skits using the situations discussed in Step 3. The skits should demonstrate appropriate ways for the character to deal with the situation.

LESSON 4: FEELING SCARED

Preparation/Materials

- Puppet (If you don't have any puppets for classroom use, make a simple puppet from a light-colored sock. Glue on felt features and some bits of yard for hair.)
- Practice puppet script.
- Student books

Objectives

- Students will describe feelings of fear.
- Students will identify ways to ease feelings of fear.

Background

Talking about fears helps children realize the universality of fears. Often by bringing fears out and looking at them, we help to dispel not only the specific fear but, more importantly, the fear of fear itself.

This and two other unit lessons suggest the use of a puppet. If you do not have puppets readily available, consider making a puppet for teaching health. Puppets are an excellent way to present situations in affective education. Students love them, and they help spark interest and make the situations come to life. Consider making and naming a puppet (we use the names Max and Mindy by turns) or having the class name the puppet. Students can also use puppets to reenact scenes or situations.

• •

Lesson

1. Use the puppet Max to explore in more detail the feeling of fear. Begin by engaging Max in a conversation about fears that are prompted by the imagination. Have Max remember a time when he was frightened by some fantasy character in children's literature or a television program.

> Teacher: Max, have you ever been scared?
>
> Max: Of course. Everyone gets scared sometimes. When I was little I was afraid of a toy bear my sister gave me for my birthday. I though it looked mean. I took it and put it in the closet so I wouldn't have to look at it. But even then, when I was in bed, I'd think about the bear in my closet. I'd imagine that it would get bigger and bigger and come out of the closet growling. I used to hide under my blanket.
>
> Teacher: That must have been scary. When did you stop being afraid of the bear?
>
> Max: One day my sister took the bear out of the closet and started pretending the bear was a clown. She made the bear do all kinds of funny things. We laughed and had fun with the bear. After that, I wasn't afraid of the bear any more.

Invite students to tell Max about fears based in fantasy that they had when they were younger, and have Max give appropriate responses or continue to interact with the puppet to tell one of your childhood fears. Stress that everyone in the whole world experiences fear at one time or another.

Next, talk with Max about the fear we often feel when we do new things.

> Teacher: You know, Max, sometimes I feel a little afraid when I'm going to try something new.
>
> Max: Mmmmmm. What do you mean? You mean eating a new kind of cake? Why would you be afraid of eating cake?
>
> Teacher: No, I don't mean that—although sometimes, I'd rather just eat things I know I like. I'm talking about being afraid of doing something I've never done before. For example, water skiing (or other activity of choice). I've never gone water skiing, and I think I'd be scared to try it. It looks hard.
>
> Max: But it's not.
>
> Teacher: How do you know?
>
> Max: Well, I've gone water skiing, and I love it. I love skimming over the top of the water. Of course, I had to learn how to put on the skis. And how to hold on to the rope the right way. And how to stand on the skis right. And a few other things, too.
>
> Teacher: I guess I'm afraid that I won't be able to do it very well. Weren't you afraid?
>
> Max: Well, at first I was. But once I tried it I wasn't afraid anymore. And at first I fell off the skis a lot. But now that I know how, I love it.

Again, interact with the class. Comment that most people are afraid of doing new things. Invite students to name things that they were afraid to do at first, but later learned to do (swimming and diving, riding a bike, etc.).

Finally, have a conversation with Max about other real fears and what we can do to help when we are frightened. Make the point that being afraid of dangerous things can help keep us safe.

> Max: You know, yesterday when my friends and I were playing together, I was afraid to do something.
>
> Teacher: What was that?
>
> Max: We were in Thorp's backyard and we were climbing on some wooden boxes behind their garage. Thorp dared me to jump from the top of the pile of boxes. It was a long way down, and I was afraid to jump.
>
> Teacher: Max, if it was dangerous to jump, I'm glad you were afraid. Sometimes being afraid helps to keep us safe. When we're afraid, our body tenses up and gets ready to move quickly to get out of a dangerous situation.

Continue interacting with the puppet or with the class and talk about what can help when we feel afraid. Sometimes we can overcome our fear by doing the very thing we're afraid of (if it's not dangerous). Some scared feelings are helped by talking with a family member, teacher, or other trusted person. End by talking about why it helps to tell God about feeling scared.

Alternative option: Drawing on children's literature, read to the class an appropriate story about being frightened. One suggestion is the chapter "The Baddest Witch in the World" from *Ramona the Pest* by Beverly Cleary.

2. **Student book.** Read the section in the student book entitled "Dealing with Feelings." Discuss only the first two questions of each "Think It Over" section.

3. Have students form groups and decide what advice they would give advice to Max and Mindy. What do they think Max could do to get over his unreasonable fear of dogs? What should Mindy do about the bullies? Have student groups answer questions 3 and 4 of the first set of questions.

    1. *He was afraid of the big dog.*
    2. *Worse. Dogs usually run after someone who is running.*
    3. *Answers will vary.*
    4. *Answers will vary.*

    1. *Afraid, upset, angry, etc.*
    2. *Answers will vary.*

    In a full class session consider and discuss the groups' suggestions. Some points to bring out in the discussion:
    - There are situations when there is reason to be afraid. Dogs *may* bite. There *are* bullies on playgrounds. On the other hand, some people are afraid of all kinds of things—caterpillars, worms, moths, etc. Students should be careful of strange dogs, but acting in panic only makes the situation worse. Often—as in the puppet scene about new things—we need to find out more, and that helps us to get over or to control our fear.
    - It helps to talk to someone we trust about our fears. Keeping fears secret is not a good idea. Ask: "Who could Mindy talk to about the bullies? Who could Max talk to about his fear of dogs?" Emphasize that if one person doesn't help, then try talking to another.

4. Ask class members to write a page for their personal books on feeling afraid. Provide a starter sentence: It scares me when...

5. Summarize/evaluate with the following questions:
    - "Why do you think people are afraid of doing something new?" (Afraid it will be too hard; afraid that they won't be able to do it well.)
    - "Is it ever good to be afraid? Why or why not?"
    - "What can help when we feel afraid?" (Talking about our feelings with others; doing what we're scared of doing.)

6. **Closure.** Sing "Wherever I Am, God Is."

● ●

Related Activities

1. Read and discuss *Where the Wild Things Are* by Maurice Sendak and/or other stories on the lesson theme.

2. Make crayon resist pictures of fears based on imaginary characters.

3. Focus on a particular aspect of fear: worry. Help students to get a Christian perspective on worry: God, who is love, is in control of the world and guides our lives. Consider telling a Bible story related to the theme of God's protection and care (for example, the saving of the baby Moses by Egyptian royalty or the escape of the Israelites from Egypt by crossing the Red Sea).

4. Memorize verses from the Bible that speak about God's care for us. Choose verses from passages such as John 14:1–4 or Luke 12:22–32. The class could also make posters illustrating the verses.

LESSON 5: FEELING HURT

Preparation/Materials
- Puppet
- Practice puppet script.

Objectives
- Students will describe hurt feelings.

- Students will identify ways to deal with hurt feelings.
- Students will choose to say they're sorry when they have hurt others' feelings.

• •

Lesson

1. Use a puppet to gently explore a sensitive area—hurt feelings.

> Teacher: Mindy, what's the matter?
> Mindy: Oh, I'm feeling down.
> Teacher: I can see that, Mindy. Do you want to talk about it?
> Mindy: Maybe you can help me think of a way to change something I did. Maybe not.
> Teacher: I'll help you if I can.
> Mindy: I said something mean about Angela to Freddie. Then Freddie told Angela. I know I hurt her feelings. Now I don't know what to do. I wish I hadn't been mean.

Break out of interaction with the Mindy to talk about the situation with the class. Ask: "What can Mindy do to try to change the situation?" Use student suggestions to finish the dialogue with Max. (Students will most likely suggest that Mindy say she's sorry. Perhaps you can send Mindy off to apologize, and then have her come back and tell you what happened when she talked to Angela.)

Alternative option: Pretend to be Mindy and give a first-person account of what you said about Angela to Freddie and how you feel about it.

2. **Circle discussion.** Open the discussion by having students describe how Mindy felt after she was mean. Then ask them how they think Angela felt and what she thought when Freddie passed on the mean remark to her. Note that probably everyone has had hurt feelings because of something mean that was said or done to them. Note also that the class probably has a good sense of the way Angela felt. Use questions such as the following to talk about hurt feelings:

- "How might Angela have responded to Mindy's mean remark?" (Encourage students to think of constructive ways to respond to mean remarks. Angela could tell Mindy, "I feel upset because you said mean things about me." Help the class to understand how destructive responses make the situation worse.)

- "How do you think Mindy felt after she said she was sorry?"
- "How do you think Angela felt after Mindy said she was sorry?"
- "Why do people say and do mean things?"
- "What does it mean to forgive?"
- "Why do we need to forgive each other?" (We forgive each other because God has forgiven us in Christ.)
- "Is it hard to forgive others who have been mean?" (Sometimes it may be difficult, but God's Spirit makes it possible.)

3. Close the circle session by teaching students the song "We Come to Ask Forgiveness" (see next page).

4. Have students write in their "feelings books" about feeling hurt. Suggested starter sentence: I feel hurt when...

   If the class is not making a booklet, assign a writing activity in which students summarize the lesson and give a personal response. Write the following two sentence starters on the board for students to complete/elaborate on.
   - Today we talked about...
   - My special thoughts are...

   Volunteers can share their writing with the rest of the class.

5. Close by summarizing the lesson. Tell students that this lesson was a little sad, but during the next lesson they'll be doing a lot of laughing.

• •

Related Activity

- Have students use puppets to plan and give skits about hurt feelings. Make this a group activity, or make up one story as a class and have students take turns acting it out.

We Come to Ask Forgiveness

Carey Landry

Chorus

We come to ask your for-give-ness, O Lord, and we seek for-give-ness from each oth-er.— Some-times we build up walls in-stead of bridg-es to peace, and we ask your for-give-ness, O Lord.

Verses

Some-times we hurt by what we do to oth-ers.— Some-times we
For the times when we've been rude and self-ish;— for the

hurt with words that are un - true.— Some-times we cause oth-ers pain by
times when we have been un - kind;— and for the times we re-fused to

what we fail to do and we ask your for-give-ness, O Lord.
help our friends in need, we— ask your for-give-ness, O Lord.

LESSON 6: HUMOR—THE BEST MEDICINE

Preparation/Materials
- Find a humorous story to read or tell or a video to show.
- Student books
- Optional: puppet

Objectives
- Students will become aware of the way humor affects feelings.
- Students will distinguish between laughing with and laughing at.

Background

Humor is one of God's delightful gifts to us. Being able to see the humor in a situation, even one in which we ourselves look ridiculous, is a wonderful gift. A person who can laugh at himself or herself or who can defuse a tense situation with gentle humor is a blessing to others. And Christians should surely be able to laugh and not take themselves too seriously. After all, Christians recognize their true place in the overall scheme of things, so they can relax and see the absurdities of life. Besides, those in the health professions tell us that people who have a sense of humor are healthier as well as happier.

● ●

Lesson

1. Tell students that in this lesson they're going to have fun and laugh together. Ask: "Aren't you glad that God made us so that we can laugh?" Note that laughter affects our feelings. Lead students to recall how Max's sister did funny things with the bear to help Max get over his feelings of fear (Lesson 4). Ask: "Can you think of other ways humor can affect our feelings?" (Cheers us up when we're upset, makes us feel friendly toward those laughing with us, may help us forget and get over angry feelings.)

   Optional: If you and your class have been enjoying Max and Mindy, consider using a puppet to introduce the lesson and tell about a funny experience.

2. Read a funny story or poem, tell a humorous personal incident, or show a funny video. Make this an enjoyable time for the class.

3. **Student book.** Then have students turn to the student book, to the section entitled "Your Funny Bone." Read aloud to the class the poem "Daddy Fell into the Pond" by Alfred Noyes.

   Explain words that students don't understand (refer to "Word Helps"). Then read the poem again. Ask students to describe the scene of the poem. Answer the "Think It Over" questions.

   1. *Gloomy, uninteresting.*
   2. *Daddy fell into the pond.*

3. *The family became merry; the gardener doubled up from laughter; the ducks quacked crazily.*
4. *Answers will vary. Most likely laughed also.*

Ask: "Do you think the person who fell into the pond laughed?" (Probably. The tone of the poem is good-natured. The others weren't laughing at the father, but with him.) Help students understand the distinction between laughing *with* and laughing *at*. Laughing at other's misfortunes or laughing at someone who is embarrassed or ashamed is hurtful: "Sometimes when something embarrassing happens, we don't feel like laughing. But later on, when we feel better, then we can laugh with others about it. What are some things we can do or say to make someone who is embarrassed feel better?"

3. Have students share stories about funny or embarrassing incidents—real or imagined. Consider making this a writing assignment.

   Alternative option: Have students write in their feelings books. Suggested starter sentences: I like to laugh because... or When I laugh I feel...

• •

Related Activities

1. Have books of humor available for students to enjoy. Include nonsense poetry, tall tales, and joke books in the collection. Give students opportunities to share their favorites.

2. Students may enjoy creating illustrated versions of "Daddy Fell into the Pond" or other humorous poems. They can copy the poem onto a poster board and then sketch the illustrations. Display the posters in the classroom.

LESSON 7: MAKING FRIENDS

Preparation/Materials
- Write the Step 3 questions on a transparency or on the board. Or write each group's questions on a slip of paper.
- Chart paper
- Student books
- Student Activity
- Optional: overhead projector

Objectives
- Students will describe feelings of being left out.
- Students will identify and describe qualities and actions that promote friendship.

• •

Lesson (2–3 sessions)

1. Recall the unit title—"Getting Along with Myself and Others." Ask students how they think what they have learned so far will help them get along with others. (Previous lessons have covered what to do if we hurt others' feelings, how to be considerate and not laugh at others in embarrassing situations, and how to enjoy laughing with others. Knowing how we feel and think in pleasant/unpleasant situations helps us understand how others feel in similar situations.) Explain that in the next lessons students will be thinking about some important problems having to do with getting along with others.

2. **Student book.** Have students read "Getting Along With Others." Use the "Think It Over" section to talk with the class about what it means to live in community.

    1. *A group of people living together. Help students identify communities to which they belong.*
    2. *Answers will vary. Discuss the effect of sin on relationships.*
    3. *Jesus came to earth for us and died on the cross for us. Jesus healed the sick and blessed people while he was on earth. Jesus still is with us.*
    4. *Answers will vary. Encourage students to go beyond the book's suggestions and to give specific examples of caring, sharing, etc.*

    Read aloud the poems "Together" and "Outside." The poems describe strong feelings about having and needing friends. Talk about the poems together; ask students to describe the situation in each poem (in "Together" a close companion and happy friendship colors and brightens all of life; in "Outside" the person desperately wants a friend, wants to be included in a circle of friends). Use the "Think It Over" questions to stimulate discussion about friendship. Tell students that today they'll be talking about the problem of being "outside."

    1. *Happy, glad to have a friend.*
    2. *Lonely, left out; others are excluding the person from the "inner circle."*

3. Divide students into small groups. Have each group sit together and be prepared to work with paper and pencil. Select a recorder and spokesperson for each group. Then introduce the topic by telling students that they are going to talk about a person—an imaginary person—named Lee (avoid using the name of a class member), who has a problem. Then tell Lee's story using local names/information to make it specific and of interest to students. Include the following facts.

    *   Lee is a new student at your school whose family recently moved into your area.
    *   Lee doesn't have any friends; she misses all the friends she had.
    *   Somehow children here don't like the way she talks and acts. She doesn't seem to be able to make friends.

4. Give each group the following questions to answer (if you prefer, give each group only one of the questions; for example, if you have six groups, assign two groups the same question). Write the questions on the board, or have them prepared on slips of paper.
    *   Question 1: What feelings do you think Lee might be having?
    *   Question 2: How do you think Lee might be acting that makes others not want to be friends?
    *   Question 3: What are ways in which you like friends to act?

    Allow students about 10 minutes to discuss the questions and write down the answers. Groups will function better if you assign a recorder, reporter, and chairperson for each group. Be available or circulate to assist groups that need help.

5. Ask groups to present their findings to the rest of the class. Have chart paper prepared for listing student suggestions.
    *   Question 1: List group suggestions of how Lee may be feeling.
    *   Question 2: Have students give their ideas of things that are preventing Lee from making friends. List and discuss these behaviors. If student list is incomplete, add to the list by eliciting further suggestions from the group.
    *   Question 3: List qualities/behaviors of friends. Again, add to the list as necessary.

6. **Student activity.** Have students make up a recipe for being a friend. First, elicit from students what recipes are. Give an example (ingredients needed, etc.). Brainstorm terms commonly used in recipes (mix, add, measure, beat, spread, bake) and write them on the board for easy reference. Then have students reflect on what makes a friend and write their recipes. You may wish to have student pairs work together on the assignment. (If students have difficulty getting started, you may wish to brainstorm a list of ingredients such as love, loyalty, humor, honesty.)

    Have students share their recipes. What ingredients did students most value? What ingredients are the hardest to offer?

    Consider putting the recipes together to make a "Friendship Cookbook." Or use the recipes to make a "Recipes for Friendship" bulletin board.

7. **Closure.** Tell students that in this lesson the class worked together to help Lee learn something about how to be a friend. Ask: "What three things did we talk about?" (How people feel when they're left out, what people do that make others not want to be friends with them, and what are ways to be friends.) Recall that the class also talked about how others in the class could befriend Lee.

• •

Related Activities

1. Students working in pairs or groups can give role-plays showing negative/positive factors and qualities of friends listed and discussed in Step 4.

2. Integrate with language arts. Have students write a paragraph on being a friend. If the class has been making feelings books, add these paragraphs to students' feelings books.

   Suggested topics:
   What I like best about my friends
   The kind of friend I'd like to be
   I make new friends by...

3. Provide a selection of books on the topic of friendship for students to enjoy. Make a particular effort to include books that show cross-cultural or intergenerational friendships. Have students contribute to the discussion on friendship by sharing their books in various ways with the rest of the class (recording brief summaries for others to listen to, making illustrations of the book characters and briefly describing the friendship for the rest of the class, reading the same book as a classmate and acting out a scene together, writing about a character in a novel that the student would like to have as a friend). Suggested books: *Rosie and Michael* by Judith Viorst, *The White Marble* by Charlotte Zolotow, *A Friend Can Help* by Terry Berger, *Making Friends* by Margaret Mahy, *Moving Molly* by Shirley Hughes, *All I See* by Cynthia Rylant, *Stay Away from the Junkyard!* by Tricia Tusa. For more titles see Lesson Resources.

LESSON 8: FRIENDLY ACTS

Preparation/Materials
- Student books
- Student Activity

Objectives
- Students will recognize that many kinds of friendships enrich life.
- Students will extend friendly acts to others.

Background
This lesson continues the topic of friendship. Lesson 7 focused on being left out. This lesson makes students aware of how a variety of friends enriches our lives. It also actively promotes friendship among class members by pairing students who normally are not close friends.

• •

Lesson

1. **Student book.** Begin the lesson by reading the poem "Wilburforce Fong" by X. J. Kennedy from the section "All Kinds of Friends." Read the poem through once for the class. Ask volunteers to tell what the poem is about. Reread the poem and answer the "Think It Over" questions.

   1. *Most likely because Wilburforce is different from the writer—and from the rest of the class.*
   2. *The writer discovered how delicious egg rolls are!*
   3. *Lead a discussion on the value/enjoyment of loving many kinds of friends. Being a friend of Wilburforce may open a new world to the writer, a world of Chinese-American traditions and customs as well as foods.*

   Encourage students to talk about "new worlds" that friends have opened to them. Also lead students to understand the enjoyment of intergenerational friendships. Tell or encourage students to tell of friendships with others younger or older than themselves.

   Next read the poem "Stephen" by Jeff Moss. What is the situation described in this poem? Use the "Think It Over" questions as a springboard for discussion. Talk about how being included in the party will make Stephen feel.

   4. *Callie spoke up and made the children see that Stephen wasn't that different from the rest of them. All of them had weaknesses as well as strengths.*
   5. *Answers will vary.*

2. **Circle discussion.** Discuss the importance of acts of kindness. Focus on the role of kindness in friendship. Broaden the discussion to include acts of kindness to those who are not our friends.

   Give students the opportunity to recall and tell about kind deeds others have done for them and how they felt as a result.

Stress that by treating others with kindness we show that we care about them. Why should we be kind to others? Realizing that God has been kind to us—welcoming us as his children—makes us want to be kind to others.

3. **Student activity.** To make this lesson concrete, have students use the coupons to plan and carry out friendly and kind acts.

   One suggestion: have class members work with partners on the activity, pairing students who normally do not seek each other out. Each pair can plan an act of kindness to do together for someone in their school or neighborhood.

   If students need more ideas for kind acts they could do, spend some time brainstorming. Give students opportunities in subsequent sessions to talk about what they did and how it affected others.

4. Consider spreading kindness to all class members through a "secret friend" plan. Each student has the name of a class member for whom they must do kind acts in secret for a week. (Students can draw names, or you can match students.) To assure that everyone is treated somewhat equally, suggest that each student give the following three things:
   - A friendly note honestly complimenting the secret friend:
     Illustration:
     > You are good at_____.
     > I like it when you _____.
   - A gift of food/snack such as gum.
   - A gift of some small item belonging to the giver that he or she is willing to give away.

• •

Related Activities

1. Tell the story of David and Mephibosheth recorded in 2 Samuel 9, and tie it in to the lesson. Note: in verse 3 David talks about wanting to show "God's kindness" to someone of Saul's house.

2. Follow up on the activity by having students write about one of their friendly acts coupons—what they did and what the response was.

3. Plan a service project for the class. Perhaps they can visit a nearby home for the elderly and sing or put on skits or a puppet show.

4. Find a way for students to express appreciation to those who show kindness to them. Make cards of appreciation for school staff members. Mention specific acts of kindness for which students are expressing thanks.

5. Read *Brave Irene* by William Steig to the class. Although this is a simple book, children will enjoy the illustrations and text about a brave trip through a blizzard to do a kind deed.

6. Make resources on the lesson topic available to the class. *Everett Anderson's Friend* by Lucille Clifton is a delightful poem about a boy who overcomes his initial distrust of his new neighbors to become fast friends. Jeff Moss's poems "Rhoda," "Laura," and "Rachel" in *The Butterfly Jar* all describe different kinds of friends.

LESSON 9: ACTIVE LISTENING

Preparation/Materials

- For "Listen Up" activity:
  cotton balls, about 40–45
  spatulas, 2–3
  paper plates, 2–3
  blindfolds, 2–3
- Chart paper
- Optional: Arrange to have an older student assist with role-play in Step 3.

Objectives

- Students will identify the roles of speaker and listener in communication.
- Students will differentiate between poor listening and active listening.
- Students will practice/observe active l istening.

Lesson (1–2 sessions)

1. Open the lesson with an activity to spark discussion of important elements of communication. Suggested activities:

Listen up!

Tell students that in this activity they will work in pairs to move cotton balls from one place to another. Show them how to scoop up cotton balls with a spatula and then put them on a paper plate. Explain that the only catch is that the student moving the balls is blindfolded while the other student is giving directions. Other rules: the blindfolded student must use one hand only and may not ask any questions; the student who does the directing may not touch the balls or the partner's arm; the pair has one minute to move as many balls as they can onto the plate. If you wish, have a student scorekeeper write down how many balls each pair successfully moves.

Have the class sit in a large circle and have two or three pairs at a time do the activity in the center of the circle. (Place balls and a paper plate within reach of each blindfolded student. If this appears to be too easy for your class, move the objects a bit farther away.) Encourage those in the circle to observe how different pairs communicate and plan for their turn.

Discuss the activity and what it teaches about communication.
- "Which student was the listener and which the speaker?"
- "Is the listener or speaker more important in communication? Or are both equally important?"
- "Did the listeners want to ask questions of the speakers? Why? Is it important to ask questions when you're listening to a speaker?"
- "Did the first pairs have a harder time than those who had watched the activity for a while? If so, why? If not, why not?"
- "How did it help when speakers gave a response to listeners' actions?"

- "What was the most frustrating part of this activity?"
  Adapted from *Listening: the Basic Connection* by Mary Micallef (Good Apple, 1984).

Mirror, Mirror
In this activity a pair of students face each other and imitate each other's actions. The goal is to make the movement as simultaneous as possible. Students can each take a turn being the leader. Abrupt, quick actions are hard to follow, so suggest using smooth, flowing motions. Maintaining eye contact is also important. As students get proficient at mirroring, have them try one final exercise in which both contribute to the movement.

Demonstrate the activity for the class before they try it. Afterward talk about how they communicated. Lead students to discover the elements of good communication that they practiced: paying close attention, being "tuned in," maintaining eye contact, etc. Adapted from *Friendly Classroom for a Small Planet* by Prutzman and others (New Society Publishers, 1988)

2. Discuss and list on chart paper the elements of good communication discovered in the Step 1 activity. The list will most likely include the following: looking at the speaker/making eye contact, paying attention to speaker/"tuning in" to the other person, responding so that person knows you're paying attention.

3. Next, role-play various poor listening (or non-listening) behaviors. Before the role-play, tell students to both listen to what's being said and to watch how you act in order to discover the poor listening behaviors. Ask a student in your class (or if this is too difficult for your students have an older student take part in the role-play) to talk to you on a topic of interest while you exhibit poor listening (for example, looking away from speaker, doodling with something else, making comments that show you haven't been listening, interrupting to talk about your own concerns).

   After the role-play, ask the speaker how it felt to be treated in that way and why. (Bring out that not listening to others gives the feeling that you're not interested in them or in their interests/activities.)

4. Make a list of poor listening behaviors on the board. Add to the list of good listening behaviors started in Step 2 (for example, avoiding things that distract, thinking about what a person is saying, not interrupting).

   In the discussion bring out the role of active listening in making and keeping friends.

5. **Student activity—concentric circles.** "Divide the class into two groups. One group makes an inner circle, and the others form a circle around this group. The people in the outer circle watch as the inner circle breaks up into pairs and discusses any topic (favorite foods, favorite activities, why people shouldn't eat junk food) of general interest to the class. The outer circle watches for active listening behavior. After 5–10 minutes stop the conversation and have the observers report to the class on positive listening behaviors. Alternatively the observers can report directly to the person or pair they were watching." (*The Collaborative Classroom* by Susan and Tim Hill [Heinemann, 1990]).

6. **Closure.** Refer to (or have a student read) the list of active listening behaviors. Erase the list of poor listening behaviors, and make the point that these are behaviors we want to avoid. End by asking: "What does 'do unto others as you would have them do unto you' have to do with listening?"

● ●

Related Activities

1. Follow Step 3 with student role-plays of active listening behaviors.

2. Ask students to write about the lesson topic in their feelings books. Suggested starters:
   I like it when someone listens to me because…
   When my best friend doesn't listen to me, I feel…

3. To further encourage students to practice active listening, have students identify specific times and ways they can begin being better listeners. Make a worksheet similar to the following.

Be an Active Listener!
I want to become an active listener. This is what I am going to do:
When I am with my friends, I will:
At home I am going to:
A listening habit I want to change is:

LESSON 10: RESOLVING CONFLICTS

Preparation/Materials
- Student Activities 1 and 2
- Unit Evaluation
- Optional: Make a transparency of the activity sheet.
- Optional: overhead projector

Objectives
- Students will become aware that they have options when they have conflicts with others.
- Students will practice solving conflicts.

Background

The activity for this lesson may be difficult for some grade 3 classes—particularly if the lesson is taught at the beginning of the school year. Using the overhead projector and working through one conflict example in some detail will probably be necessary. If the group work still seems too difficult, consider doing one or two situations in a whole class session.

One lesson on conflict resolution will help to make students aware that there are various ways of dealing with problems and it will help them to begin thinking about what to do in cases of conflict; however, most teachers find that to make serious changes they must make conflict resolution part of the daily round. Daily sharing circles are good times to talk about conflicts and how to resolve them. The discussion need not be heavy; using humor in class is a good way to help students take petty conflicts less seriously and to teach them how humor can defuse potential conflicts.

If you wish to spend more time during this unit on conflict resolution, you may wish to try the approach of a grade 4 teacher that was written up in *Friendly Classroom for a Small Planet*. This teacher used Ezra Jack Keats's book *Goggles* as a basis for discussion and was amazed at the sustained discussion and interest of his class. On the first day the teacher sketched the conflict in the story (without giving away the ending), and the students brainstormed possible solutions (they came up with 40!). The students copied the solutions into their notebooks and discussed them, deciding which were workable and why. On the second day the teacher read the story to the class, and students individually chose what they thought were the three best solutions. On the third day the students discussed their choices, including which solutions would lead to violence and which would not.

Lesson (2–3 sessions)

1. Write the word *conflict* on the board, and ask students what it means (a fight or disagreement between two or more people). Give an example of a conflict (two people want to use the same ball at the same time). Ask: "How do you think people in a conflict may be feeling?"

   Tell students that in this lesson they are going to think about some conflicts that people might have. Some of the conflicts will be between friends. They will be working in groups to settle or resolve the conflicts.

2. **Student activity.** Divide the class into groups and refer to Student Activity 1 in the student workbook. The students may cut apart the conflict cards and use them with Student Activity 2. As an option, you may want to use an overhead projector to show a sample activity sheet and to demonstrate how students are to work together to solve a problem dealing with a conflict. Use one of the conflict cards as an example and explain how to fill in the sample form.

   Have the groups work together to resolve a conflict. Give each group a card describing a conflict. Be sure to use conflicts that are appropriate for your class. If you wish, use the suggestions listed below. Make the conflict situations concrete and specific by naming characters and places.

   Each group should discuss its situation and fill in the worksheet.

3. Have the group reporter read the conflict card and the group's worksheet to the rest of the class. Talk about the group's decision. Is their solution a good way to settle the conflict? Why or why not? (If students make inappropriate suggestions, ask: "What might happen as a result?") Suggest things that students could do to feel better. Stress that when we're upset about something, we shouldn't act hastily, and if we're upset about a problem it's a good idea to talk with a trusted adult about it.

4. **Circle discussion.** Talk about dealing with feelings of anger and frustration. Points to include in the discussion on the topic of anger:
   • Anger is an emotion everyone has.
   • It's not wrong to get angry, but it's wrong to act irresponsibly when we're angry. Even if the other person has done something unfair or mean to us, it's wrong for us to hurt them.
   • It helps to cool down before we act. Responding hastily can make the situation worse. Counting to 10 before acting is a good idea.
   • It's good to tell others that we're angry and what we're angry about. It helps them to understand our feelings and actions. Express angry emotion in an "I feel..." statement. For example, "When you're bossy, I feel upset."
   • It's important not to stay angry. Staying angry inside will build walls between us and others and between us and God. When we hold grudges, we're really nursing the anger we have toward that person. God tells us to forgive others *because* God has forgiven us. (Recall the discussion in lesson 5 on hurt feelings.) You may also wish to bring in Ephesians 4:26b—"Do not let the sun go down while you are still angry."

   Close the discussion by summarizing or eliciting from students a summary of the lesson concepts.

5. If the class is composing feelings books, have them write their last page in response to the lesson topic. Suggested starters: I feel upset when…; Knowing that God forgives me makes me feel…; When others forgive me I feel…

   Give students the opportunity to make covers for their books before they take them home.

6. **Unit evaluation**. Use the worksheet to review and evaluate.

   Short essay:
   1. *Facial expression, body language, tone of voice.*
   2. *Answers will vary but might include talking to others about our feelings, and if we have hurt others, saying we're sorry.*
   3. *Answers will vary. Students may suggest overcoming fear of new things by trying to do them, talking with a friend or trusted adult, and talking to God.*
   4. *Answers will vary, but might include expressing feelings in a non-blameful way, talking to someone about feelings, thinking or doing something enjoyable.*
   5. *Answers will vary.*

   Sentence completion:
   1. *Answers will vary, but might include looking away, doodling, interrupting, not paying attention.*
   2. *Answers will vary, but may include looking at the speaker, paying attention, responding.*
   3. *she had been mean to others.*
   4. *a fight or disagreement between two or more people.*
   5. *upset or angry/answers will vary.*
   6. *Staying angry will build walls between us and others and between us and God; angry feelings bottled up inside can give us headaches and stomachaches or can make us feel tired.*

7. Close the unit by singing the unit songs, "Wherever I Am, God Is" and "We Come to Ask Your Forgiveness," and other appropriate class favorites.

• •

Related Activity

• Make books available for students to read on the lesson topic. See the resources section.

Unit 3

Living in a Family

Goals

- Students will develop their understanding of family life and the part they play in it.
- Students will develop their understanding of the human life cycle and life before birth.
- Students will develop their Christian understanding of death.

Background

The family is part of our loving God's plan for human life. Scripture affirms this throughout (see, for example, Psalm 127:3–5). But marriage and family life have not escaped the effects of sin. Because of sin, barriers form between family members, and family ties are broken. Because of sin, family life is not what God intended. Children as well as adults live with sin's effects in the family, and it is not helpful to our students to gloss over reality and pretend that family life is trouble free. Nonetheless, as we teach about family living, we can offer students a message of hope. In Christ, God is restoring his image in us. In Christ, and with the help of Christ's Spirit, we can find joy in family life. By obeying God's law of love we are able to forgive each other and treat each other with respect.

Loving each other as we would like to be loved also implies a positive self-respect. This is a good foundation for the students' developing sexual awareness. Boys and girls can appreciate their own and each other's gifts. When we operate under God's rule of love, we can also make positive changes in the way we communicate at school and at home.

Obedience to God's rule becomes easier as we deepen our understanding of God's love and care for us. God holds us in his loving hands from our mother's womb to beyond the grave. Seeing and understanding better the marvelous way in which life is created and the way God gives us new life that death cannot destroy invigorates us to image God's love in family living.

Vocabulary

Integrate the following suggested vocabulary:

negative	fetus	egg	positive	sperm
female	role	depend	sex	communicate
sexuality	resurrection	male	grief	grieving

Unit Resources (Search online for similar resources if these are no longer available)

Family: Poems for Kids. Academy of American Poets. Poets.org.

Grade appropriate books about family can be found through https://shop.scholastic.com/teachers-ecommerce.

Lesson Resources (Search online for similar resources if these are no longer available)

Lesson 1

Drescher, Joan. *Your Family, My Family.* New York: Walker, 1980.

Describes various types of families with the conclusion that living together, loving, and caring are the ties that define family.

Fluornoy, Valerie. *The Patchwork Quilt.* New York: Dial, 1985.
> Grandma is using material from worn-out clothing to make a patchwork quilt of memories. When Grandma becomes sick, Tanya and her mother work on the quilt.

Girard, Linda Walvoord. *Adoption Is for Always.* Morton Grove, Ill.: Whitman, 1986.

_____. *At Daddy's on Saturdays.* Morton Grove, Ill.: Whitman/Toronto: General Publishing, 1987.
> Katie discovers that even though her parents live apart, she will maintain her loving relationship with her father. Students whose parents are divorced will find this book reassuring.

Jokston, Tony. *The Quilt Story.* New York: Putnam, 1985.
> A handmade quilt eases the loneliness of a pioneer girl; generations later the same quilt gives comfort to a young girl moving to a new town. Illustrated by Tomie dePaola. Picture book for ages 5–8.

Rylant, Cynthia. *The Relatives Came.* New York: Bradbury, 1985.
> Relatives of all shapes and sizes come for a visit. Picture book for ages 6–8.

Stinson, Kathy. *Mom and Dad Don't Live Together Anymore.* Toronto: Annick Press, 1984.

Lesson 2

Christenson, Larry. *The Wonderful Way That Babies Are Made.* Minneapolis: Bethany House, 1982.
> This book is written with two separate texts—one for children ages 3–8 and a smaller-print, more detailed version for ages 9–14. The author places sexuality firmly in the context of family and as part of the plan of a loving Creator. (Adoption and the immaculate conception of Jesus are also covered.)

Cole, Joanna. *Asking About Sex and Growing Up.* New York: Morrow, 1988.

Hummel, Ruth. *Where Do Babies Come From?* Learning About Sex Series. St. Louis: Concordia, 1982, 1988.
> Seven-year-old Suzanne learns how babies grow inside the mother and that both mother and father have a part in making a baby. Includes the following vocabulary: *uterus, navel, pregnant, vagina, vulva, penis, scrotum, testicles, sperm*. A helpful resource written from a Christian perspective and intended for children ages 6–8. One criticism: on the whole the book's approach is direct and natural, but the setting of chapter 2 in a museum is contrived.

Lesson 3

Cooney, Barbara. *Miss Rumphius.* New York: Puffin, 1985.

Nilsson, Lennart. *A Child is Born.* New York: Delacorte, 1990.
> Photographs show fetal development.

Lesson 4

"3 Ways to Teach Kids the Importance of Teamwork." Crisis Prevention Institute. https://www.crisisprevention.com/Blog/Teamwork.

Lesson 5

DeSpelder, Lynn, and Albert Strickland. *Family Life Education: Resources for the Elementary Classroom.* Grades 4, 5, 6. Santa Cruz, Calif.: Network Publications, 1982.

Lesson 6

Adoff, Arnold. *All the Colors of the Race.* New York: Lothrop, Beach Tree Books, 1992.
  A collection of poems written from the point of view of a child with a black mother and a white Jewish father.

Polacco, Patricia. *The Keeping Quilt.* New York: Simon and Schuster, 1988.
  This story is a chronicle of a quilt, sewn from scraps of an immigrant's girl's dress and babushka, which is passed down through generations of a family. Family rituals are repeated and yet changed to fit the people and times as the quilt is used.

Stevens, Carla. *Anna, Grandpa, and the Big Storm.* New York: Houghton Mifflin, 1982.
  When Anna becomes snowbound on the Third Avenue elevated train, she learns to understand her grandfather a little better and shares an adventure that she can tell her children and grandchildren. An easy-to-read story based on an actual historical event.

Lesson 7

Ieronimo, Christine. *A Thirst for Home.* Bloomsbury USA, 2014.

Diaz, Natalia et al. *A Ticket Around the World.* Owlkids Books, 2012.

Manushkin, Fran. *Latkes and Applesauce: A Hanukkah Story.* New York: Scholastic, 1990.
  A fictional account the Menashe family's Hanukkah celebration in the Soviet Union.

Stanek, Muriel. *We Came from Vietnam.* Morton Grove, Il.: Whitman, 1985.

Lesson 8

Gould, Deborah. *Grandpa's Slide Show.* New York: Lothrop, 1987.

Grollman, Earl A. *Talking About Death.* Boston: Beacon Press, 1970.

Huntley, Theresa. *Helping Children Grieve.* Minneapolis: Augsburg, 1991.

Kaldhol, Marit, and Wenche Oyen. *Goodbye Rune.* New York: Kane/Miller, 1987.

LESSON 1: THE CHRISTIAN FAMILY— GROWING IN LOVE

Preparation/Materials
- Index cards with family situations printed on them for group problem-solving exercise
- Student books
- Student Activity
- Optional: Write the "golden rule" on a large sheet of paper.

Objectives
- Students will understand God's law of love as the basis of family life.
- Students will work together to identify Christian solutions to typical family situations.
- Students will identify a specific experience of unconditional love from their own experience.

Background

God created us to live in relationship with others. We were designed to live in families. The basis of family life in a Christian household is God's law of love. We express love for God in our family prayers and Bible reading, in worshiping God with his people, and in witnessing. God's law of love also comes to expression in the day-to-day situations of family life as family members treat one another in God-pleasing ways.

Students should be aware, however, that love does not take the same form in every Christian family. Each family must choose the patterns and expressions of love that it finds comfortable and acceptable. In some families, love takes the form of quiet statements of affirmation, but in others love erupts in loud cheers and exuberant hugs.

The lesson provides students with the opportunity to celebrate true life examples of love from their own experience. And as student groups work through typical family situations, they will experience in a fresh and unique way the choices of love.

Lesson

1. Introduce the lesson by writing the unit title, "Living in a Family," on the chalkboard. Begin by describing the people in your own family group. Ask the students to offer other groupings that are a family. The students should realize that a family may be made up of people who are or are not related to each other by blood and who may or may not live in the same house.

   You may also wish to review from earlier grade levels the basic needs that are met by families: food, shelter, clothing, love, and support. Point out that *family* is defined not only by who its members are but also by what they do.

   Continue the discussion by asking the class to think about what Christian families do. Explain that in many ways Christian families do some of the same things that other families do. They go to basketball games, eat pizza, share the chores, and love and take care of each other. The difference is in the Christian family's love for God and each other. God's law of love is the basis for Christian family life.

2. Write God's law of love, "Love God with all your heart and love others the way you would like to be loved" on the board or post it on a large sheet of paper.

   Divide the class into family groups of 3–4 students each. Give each group an index card with a family situation written on it from the list below. Each "family" must work together to decide what they would do in that situation. Stress that there may be more than one right choice. What is important is that whatever course of action they choose, their actions must show that they are following God's law of love.

   You may choose to have the groups present their solutions in writing or by acting out the situation. If you are teaching this lesson in two sessions, break after the groups have made their decisions. Begin the second session with the group presentation.

   Suggested family situations:
   - Eric told his mother he would be playing at Jose's house until 5:00. Jose's big brother offered to take Eric and Jose to the park, but they probably won't be home until 5:30.
   - Amber and Ashley's parents have grown-up guests at the house. Amber wants to play with her big sister, Ashley. Ashley would rather read a book.
   - Father is offered a good job in a different city. Some people in the family want to stay, some want to move. The family needs to make a big decision.
   - Tomas got his spelling test back today. He had five wrong answers! He didn't want to tell his family because his sister and brother were both good at spelling. At dinner that night his grandma said, "Tomas, you are so quiet. Is something the matter?"
   - Usually Dad cooks dinner every night, Shaina sets the table, Mom cleans up, and Kareem takes out the garbage. But tonight Dad is in bed with a bad cold.
   - Mother's Day is only two days away. The kids—Jamie, Shawn, and Alex—want to really show their mom how much they love her. When they count their money, they find that even if they put all their money together they only have $1.57.
   - Sammy has been practicing a new piano piece for the upcoming recital. Sammy is nervous, but he remembers Mom will be there to clap—even if there are mistakes. Mom supports all of her kids' activities. For example, she has never missed one of Jesse's soccer games. Today, Jesse came home and announced that the soccer team made it to the finals. They will play for the champion title—on the same afternoon as Sammy's recital.

   After each group's presentation, talk with the class about what difference being Christian made in that particular family situation. Emphasize that love can be shown both in our words and our actions. (Although, of course, being Christian makes a difference in family life, be careful not to lead students to expect that non-Christian families are unloving and uncaring.)

3. **Student book.** Read and discuss the opening page of "Living in a Family" and "A Story About Two Brothers." Discuss the "Think It Over" questions.

   1.   *He felt that as a single person he didn't need all of his share; he wanted to help his brother who had the responsibility of caring for a family.*
   2.   *He reasoned that because the single brother was without a wife and children to care for him in the coming years, his single brother needed extra grain.*
   3.   *Answers will vary.*

4.   **Student activity.** Ask the students to recall a time from their own family experience when they really felt, or were a witness to, Christian love. Students should fill in the love award with the name(s) of the family members who were involved and should describe what happened. (If students have difficulty thinking of specific examples to use, recall some of the situations acted out in Step 2.) The students can cut these out to take them home and give to the appropriate person(s).

5.   **Closure.** Close the lesson by learning the chorus to "God Has Made Us a Family." The rest of the song may be taught as time allows with this or other lessons in the unit.

● ●

Related Activities

1.   Integrate with language arts. Two suggested activities:
   •   Have students write in their journals a list of the people in their family. Then ask them to write one way (big or small) in which they could show love to each family member.
   •   Provide magazine pictures of different family groupings. Students can choose a family picture to paste on a piece of writing paper or in their journal and then write a story about that family.

2.   Integrate with social studies. Consider studying typical family life in another country. Learn the words for *mother, father, sister, brother, grandmother,* and *grandfather* in the language of that country.

3.   Reference the resources list to reinforce or extend the lesson. *Family, My Family* by Joan Drescher.

God Has Made Us a Family

Carey Landry

LESSON 2: IN THE IMAGE OF GOD— MALE AND FEMALE

Preparation/Materials
- Student Activity
- Teacher Visual (optional)
- Student book

Objectives
- Students will understand that human sexuality is part of God's good plan.
- Students will understand that God's blessings are extended to both men and women.
- Students will understand that mothers and fathers are partners in beginning a baby.
- Students will explore the concept of gender-role behaviors and expectations.

Background
The first thing we read in Genesis about God's design for humankind is that we are all created in God's image, that is, with righteousness and holiness. As God's image bearers, we are all worthy of respect. Such self-respect is healthy, and it is the foundation for good relationships with others. That's why this lesson begins with the opportunity to affirm the individual gifts of your students.

Human sexuality is also part of God's design ("male and female he created them"), and students need to understand this, too. They need the opportunity to look at human sexuality from a Christian perspective. Our culture attacks our children from birth with skewed views of every aspect of human sexuality. It often glorifies the "body beautiful," distorts gender roles, and demeans marriage and the sex act. Students need correct and accurate information, but more than that, they need to be able to tie their sexual understanding and identity in a positive way to their belief in God. Parents and teachers can model attitudes of joy, wonder, and responsibility towards human sexuality, serving as powerful counterbalances to the views prevalent in North American society.

Be sure to inform parents in advance about what will be covered in this lesson. Good communication establishes trust and prevents misunderstandings. Schools may wish to discuss the specific content of health education at the orientation meetings at the beginning of the school year.

Lesson
1. Introduce the lesson by having students write down several things they like about themselves. Suggest they think of physical traits, talents, or interests.

   Meet in a circle to read the lists (or, if the class is large, one item from each list) aloud. Have students look for similarities and differences in what they value in themselves. Point out any similarities that could be grouped by gender.

2. Lead the group to a discussion of physical similarities and differences—first as humans and then as boys and girls. Consider using the teacher visual in the back of this Teacher's Guide to teach or review names of male and female body parts.

   Explain that the differences in our bodies are part of God's good plan. God designed men and women in this way so that when they are married they can enjoy "making love" or "having intercourse." Intercourse is a gift that God planned only for married people—a gift to build strong and loving families. During intercourse the sperm from the father enters the mother's body. Once a month the mother's body releases an egg. When a sperm and egg come together, a baby begins to grow. The baby will continue to grow inside the mother's body almost nine months until it is ready to be born.

Consider why male and female bodies are made differently. Explain that each has a different job in beginning a baby, but both are necessary and important.

Alternative option: Read *The Wonderful Way That Babies Are Made* by Larry Christenson. Read sections that deal with the same material covered in previous Step 2 paragraphs.

3. Explore gender roles. Begin by defining the idea of playing a role. Ask students what they think of when they hear the word *clown.* What kind of behavior do they expect from someone who is called a clown? A clown plays a particular role—someone who does silly things. Tell the students that sometimes people think that men and women or boys and girls have to act according to a certain role because they are male or female.

4. **Student activity.** Pass out the student activity to each student. Direct students to fill out this opinion survey and give their own ideas about gender roles. Have them complete the section for men and the section for women.

   Review the survey results either by a show of hands or by tabulating (perhaps graphing) the results on an overhead projector. Point out that if the survey were done with a similar group of students living in a different time or place, the results might be drastically different. Lead the class to understand why this is so.

   Help break down stereotypes by offering biographical sketches (from history, modern culture, or your own personal acquaintance) that are not what might be commonly expected male and female roles.

5. **Student book.** Turn to the section "Boys and Girls—Alike and Different" and read the poem "Girls Can Too!" Use the "Think It Over" questions to talk about the poem.

   1. *At doing active things such as sports, running, and so on.*
   2. *Answers will vary.*
   3. *Answers will vary. Bring out her amusement at hollow claim.*
   4. *Answers will vary.*

6. **Closure.** Read Genesis 1:27–31 and Galatians 3:26–29. Emphasize that humans were made male and female as part of God's good plan. God blessed them both and gave them mutual responsibilities. Through Christ's death we are all full members of God's family.

Related Activities

1. Raise student awareness of the roles males and females typically play. Assign students to watch a television program or read a book. Tell them to pick a male or female character and write a description of the role that character plays. (How does she or he act? What kinds of things does she or he say? What kinds of clothes does the character wear?) The students should then consider what they agree and disagree with regarding the character's behavior.

2. Use available resources to reinforce or extend the lesson. See resources list.

LESSON 3: FEARFULLY AND WONDERFULLY MADE

Preparation/Materials
- Series of photos or pictures showing a person (preferably you) from birth to the present.
- Pencils with erasers (brand new ones, sharpened only once would be best)
- Student Activity
- Construction paper, one sheet per student
- Optional: a baby doll the size of a newborn
- Optional: Make a Teacher Visual using the Student Activity as a model.
- Optional: overhead projector

Objectives
- Students will become aware of the stages of human life.
- Students will understand that every person grows and changes, beginning with the joining of two cells—one from each parent.
- Students will identify their stage of life and the stages of life of their family members

Background
God created all living creatures to be conceived, be born, grow up, change, reproduce, and die. The stages of life begin at birth, but life begins before that day. While our life here on earth can physically be traced to a sperm and ovum, God has always known us. And though our bodies may die, we will live again through Christ.

The stages of life chart, then, gives us a diagram of what our life on earth may be like. Students should be led to look beyond this model made by human hands and wonder at the mysterious and miraculous design that only God can fully comprehend.

. . . .

Lesson
1. Discuss the basic human pattern of growth and change. Begin by showing the students the series of pictures of yourself, starting with the youngest portrait. Ask them to guess who they think the child is. (If enough photos are not available of yourself, try to use photos of someone the children will know.

    After everyone has seen the photos, ask class members to look for features that stay the same as one grows. Then have them tell what physical changes take place. Talk about changes that most likely will take place in the future. Make a sketch of yourself as an older person, or ask the group to offer their ideas on what changes will take place.

    Ask the children if they have seen baby pictures of themselves. Did they ever wonder what they looked like before they were born? Recap concepts from Lesson 2: human life begins with a sperm and egg, both of which are too tiny to see.

2. Use the following activity to give students an idea of the size of a developing fetus. Distribute a new pencil to each student. Ask students to take out a scrap of paper and make a tiny dot. Explain that the sperm and egg joined together are smaller than that dot. But, that dot of life will grow and change to become a baby. By the time the fetus has been growing inside its mother for four weeks, it is as large as a pencil eraser and has a beginning heartbeat.

When the fetus has been growing inside its mother for four months, it will be as long as the shaft of the pencil (approximately 6") and will weigh as much as ¼ pound (the same weight as a well known fast-food hamburger). At this time the fetus has all the physical features it will have when it is born. Its organs need more time to grow and develop, however, before it can live outside of its mother. (*A Child Is Born* by Lennart Nilsson provides wonderful, photographic illustrations of the growth of a fetus.)

At birth a baby usually weighs about 7 pounds and is roughly 20 inches long. You may wish to show the class a baby doll to demonstrate the size of a newborn. Note that on the day of birth a baby has already been growing for nine to ten months. That's why in China people count those months when they figure a person's age. So, at birth a baby is considered to be one year old in China.

Consider having students calculate their present age using the Chinese system.

3. Use the teacher visual to introduce the stages of human life. Describe each stage in terms of physical and family changes that take place (Include head to body proportion changes, change in height, development of more pronounced male/female traits, aging—hair thinning and graying, etc.). Continue to stress that people keep changing throughout life.

4. **Student activity.** Instruct students to color and cut out the stages and glue them in proper order onto a sheet of construction paper. (Leave the visual on display for student reference.)

   Next, have students link their family members to specific life stages. Each student should make a list of family members (including any living grandparents and great-grandparents) on the back of the construction paper and then identify what stage of life each person is in, either by writing the stage of life after each family member's name or by rewriting that person's name next to the appropriate stage on the front of the sheet.

5. **Closure.** End the lesson by reading Psalm 139:13–17. Stress that God has been watching over us since before we were born. He knows our bodies and our hearts. He will continue to guard us all the days of our lives.

• •

Related Activities

1. Assign the Bible passage as memory work.

2. Using another copy of the Student Activity, have the students map goals (learning to drive, having a job, getting married, having children, retirement) for each stage of life.

3. Journal starter: What God knows about me that no one else does...

4. Read *Miss Rumphius* by Barbara Cooney. Have the students chart the curious adventures of Miss Rumphius on the stages of life chart. The same could be done for any fictional, historical, or biblical figure the class is currently studying.

LESSON 4: DEPENDING ON EACH OTHER

Preparation/Materials

- Choose one for Step 1 activity:
  a hanging mobile
  four older students to sing or play musical
      instruments (see Step 1)
- Paper for writing activity
- Student books

Objectives

- Students will understand that family members are interdependent.
- Students will identify ways that they can contribute to family life.

• •

Lesson

1. Do one of the following activities to introduce the lesson.

   - Display the hanging mobile. Blow gently on the mobile to show that even though the individual pieces vary and are free to move, they need the others to keep everything in balance. Then remove one of the pieces. The remaining units will now just hang instead of floating through the air.

   - Ask the older students to play or sing a brief section of music in harmony. Have them demonstrate that each takes a different part, but all work together. Then have each of the performers play a completely different piece of music—all at the same time. Finally ask three to play the same piece and just one person to play a different tune. What happens when players don't work together?

2. Discuss the interdependence of family members. Ask the class how a family can be like the hanging mobile or the musicians. Summarize their suggestions to explain how family members rely on each other. Introduce the word *depend*.

   Stress that for the family to work and live together in harmony family members need to be able to depend on one another for love, support, and filling certain responsibilities. Give examples.

3. **Student book.** Turn to "Depending on Each Other" and read "A Very Bad Day." After the students have read the selection, they should rewrite the story to show how each family member is fulfilling his or her responsibilities. Or they may choose to write a poetic ending in which the members begin again to take care of each other. Answer the "Think It Over" questions.

   1. *No.*
   2. *Children didn't do chores or change baby; the father didn't buy bread; mother is impatient with baby.*
   3. *Answers will vary.*

4. Finally, each student should write a list of five or six ways their family depends on them (possibilities: watching younger siblings, taking care of pets, doing household chores, taking mail to the mailbox, visiting grandparents.) Give class members ample opportunity to share their lists in a whole class session or in groups.

5. Close by singing "God Has Made Us a Family."

LESSON 5: WHAT DO YOU SAY?

Preparation/Materials
- Optional props for Step 1:
  a piece of writing paper
  toy telephone or receiver cut from paper
- Student books
- Student Activity

Objectives
- Students will develop an understanding of the importance of word choice.
- Students will choose to communicate in a caring way.

Background

This lesson focuses on communicating in a caring and constructive way. It gives students opportunity to learn about "I" messages and "you" messages. Jeanne Gibbs in his book *Tribes* (Publisher's Press, 1987) describes these messages as follows:

"An 'I' message is a statement of the speaker's feelings in response to a situation or the behavior of others. The statement, unlike a 'you' message, does not convey judgment nor is it a put-down....

"I" messages:
- State and 'own' the speaker's feelings.
- Focus on behavior, not on personal judgments.

"You" messages:
- Hold another person responsible for speaker's feelings.
- Make personal judgments; put people down.

"The purpose of an 'I' message is to communicate feelings in such a way that the other person is not forced to defend herself or avoid the situation. The impact of the 'you' message blames, shames or intimidates the other person. 'you' messages also kill self-esteem.

"We need to be aware of 'you' messages that masquerade as 'I' messages. For example, 'I feel that you are always a nuisance,' is a disguised put-down, a 'you' message because:

1. No feelings are owned even though the speaker says 'I feel' (he really means 'I think').
2. The phrase 'You are always a nuisance' is a judgment implying that the person is bad or incapable of being different.'"

Although students in grade 3 may not completely understand the intricacies of these types of messages, they surely can understand the concept of caring communication. Encourage them to consider the impact of their words on others. Of course, your own modeling of caring communication is the students' best teacher.

- -

Lesson

1. Introduce the lesson topic—communication in the family. Tell the class you have a very important message you need to get to someone in your family. Consider several options and elicit from students why each may or may not be the best way to send a message. To add interest act out each method of communication.
   - Shouting the message out of the classroom window. (Family member can't hear the message if her or she is not within range.)
   - Writing a letter to your family member. (Point out the delay in mail and not being able to hear or see the person sending the message as disadvantages.)

- Using the telephone. (This method offers more advantages, but note that you and your family member wouldn't be able to see or touch each other as you shared the important news.)
- Communicating the message person to person. (Allows for both verbal and non-verbal communication.)

2. Focus on verbal communication. Make the point that choosing the method of communicating is important and so is choosing the right words. Make students aware of the powerful impact their words have on family members. Why is caring communication important?

3. **Student book.** Introduce students to the concept of "I" messages and "you" messages and positive/negative messages. Turn to "Communicating with Family Members." Read "What Do You Say, Dear?" and "Sending 'I' Messages." Begin by discussing the difference between "you" statements and "I" statements, especially from the listener's point of view. Read all the "you" messages first and have students identify the tone of the remarks. Next read the "I" messages. What tone do they convey? Then read each pair of messages. Which would students prefer to have addressed to them and why? Add material from the background of the lesson as appropriate.

   Discuss negative and positive messages. Talk about the examples given in "Accent on the Positive," and again ask students which message they'd prefer to receive and why. (In the discussion be sure not to give the impression that "negative" feelings are not allowed.)

   Use the "Think It Over" questions to continue the discussion.

   1. *Answers will vary; however, students will probably admit that "you" messages are easier. Without making the discussion too weighty, talk about our "natural," sinful bent to put ourselves first and not concern ourselves with how our words affect others.*
   2. *Lead students to see that positive messages are not a form of flattery or dishonesty in communication. We can communicate truthfully but still work to build the other person up.*

4. Briefly touch on other tools for healthy family communication. Review communication concepts covered in Unit 2 (active listening, sharing feelings, humor). How do these ideas apply in family settings?

   Give some specific family situations, and encourage class members to use insights they've gained about communication in their responses:
   - Your mother mentions that her hours are going to be cut back at work and that some workers are being let go.
   - Your brother is carrying potatoes to the dinner table and trips, dropping the food and breaking the bowl.

- Your grandmother tells you about a friend whose husband has cancer.
- Your sister and you both want to buy new clothes. Your family doesn't have enough money for *both* of you to buy them. Your sister tells you that she's the one who needs the clothes because she's older.

5. **Student activity.** Have students complete the puzzle individually or in groups.

> *Across: 1 (active listening), 4 (love), 6 (positive), 7 (sharing)*
> *Down: 2 (cooperation), 3. ("I" messages, 5 (honor), 8 (humor)*

● ●

Related Activities

1. Locate an episode of a TV family sitcom (perhaps from classic rerun). Play some of the dialog for the class, and examine how family members are communicating. Look for examples of effective/ineffective communication.

2. Explore family styles and times of communication. What family rituals are occasions for communicating? (At meals, before bedtime, during special outings, while sharing interests.)

LESSON 6: FAMILY HERITAGE TREE

Preparation/Materials

- Before teaching the lesson, send a note home assigning students to discover and write down:

  family name (and what it means if known)

  country(ies) that ancestors came from (list up to three)

- Prepare to make a bulletin board display entitled Family Heritage Tree. Collect these materials:

  brown mural-sized paper to make a tree trunk

  brown construction paper strips for branches, one per student

  green paper leaves, at least one per student

- Make the tree trunk and mount it on a classroom bulletin board.

- Optional: Make a sample branch and leaf about your own family heritage.

Objectives

- Students will become aware of and develop appreciation for their family heritage.
- Students will develop appreciation for diverse family styles and backgrounds.

Background

The topic of family heritage may be a sensitive one for adopted children. If the issue arises, note that adopted children are part of a family in the same way everyone else is and that they will also get the information for their part of the tree by getting information from relatives. Adopted children whose national origin is different from their adoptive families may wish to write both countries of origin on their part of the classroom tree.

The idea for the lesson activity is adapted from *Family Life Education: Resources for the Elementary Classroom* by Lynn DeSpelder and Albert Strickland.

• •

Lesson

1. Introduce the lesson topic, family heritage. Tell the class that they will be building a family heritage tree.

   Explain what a family heritage is. Consider saying something similar to the following: "*Heritage* is a word that is used to describe something that is handed down to you from the people who lived before you in your family. Your last name is a good example of something handed down to you from your parents and grandparents. Your heritage can be related to the country where your parents or grandparents were born. For example, the foods you eat (especially on holidays) may be foods commonly eaten in those countries. (Give examples. Include different ways of doing things or dressing.) Sometimes objects can be part of your family heritage. Family rituals—the pattern or way you always do things are part of your heritage. Family stories, those stories about people in your family that you hear told over and over again, are a rich part of your heritage."

Show students the prepared bulletin board with the tree trunk. Write the class name, grade, or room number on it. Note that this tree will be unique because each family is unique. The completed tree will show something of each student's heritage on its branches and leaves.

2. Work with the class to construct the tree.
    *   Give each student a tree branch. Direct students to clearly write their family name, its meaning (if known), and the countries of the family's origin on the branch. If you have prepared a sample, show it to the class to use as a model.
    *   Next have students write something about their family heritage on the prepared leaves.

Before distributing the leaves, tell something about your own family's unique customs or traditions. Use the following questions to help students decide on a custom/tradition/family story of their family to write about.
*   "Is there a special story your family loves to hear and tell, a story most other people don't know?"
*   "Does your family have special things you do at Christmas (time of sharing gifts, picking a tree, singing certain songs, eating certain foods), Thanksgiving Day, or Easter?"
*   "Does your family celebrate holidays or other special days many other North Americans don't?" (Chinese New Year, special family remembrance days)
*   "Is there some special place your family loves to visit?"

Give students time to brainstorm individual lists of ideas and choose one to write on their leaf.

3. Assemble the tree. Students should take turns reading their branches and leaves aloud to the class as they come forward to offer their contribution to the family heritage tree.

•••

Related Activities

1. Read selections that relate to the lesson topic with the class. You may wish to do this before making the tree. Reference the resources list.

2. Consider asking members of various classroom families to tell the class more about their heritage or to share mementoes, pictures, or songs with the class.

3. Read selections from Arnold Adoff's *All the Colors of the Race.* "Borders," "I Know We Can Go Back So Far," "Still Finding Out," and "Four Foot Feat" are poems that tie in with the theme of this lesson. Or, have the class read other poems about diversity and inclusion.

LESSON 7: DIFFERENT CULTURES AND LIVING PATTERNS

Preparation/Materials

- Student Activity
- Optional: Invite someone who has lived abroad to visit your class and speak about family lifestyles in that country.

Objectives

- Students will develop an increased aware-ness of the difference in family backgrounds.
- Students will develop a greater appreciation for different times/cultures.

Lesson

1. Introduce the class to the idea that family life varies with time, location, and individuals. Tell them about things you did as a child that are similar to and different from the things your students do. Or invite a guest speaker to tell about family life in a foreign country.

2. **Student activity.** Refer to the interview worksheets and explain the assignment. Read over the directions and interview questions with the class. Make sure students under-stand that the family member should be from an older generation. Students should complete the intergenerational interview as homework.

    Lead a class discussion on student findings. What is most surprising about the answers? Summarize any similarities that show up as you read through the results (for example, size of families, number of at-home mothers, changes in technology, etc.). Consider graphing responses to questions 3, 4, and 5.

    Note: The worksheet is adapted from *Family Life Education: Resources for the Elementary Classroom* by DeSpelder and Strickland (Network, 1982).

    Bind the interviews into a class book. (You may wish to have each student provide an illustration to accompany their interview sheet, showing the way they imagine things were.)

3. **Closure.** Ask students to call out one new thing they learned about the various ways families can live together and take care of each other. Encourage appreciation for and acceptance of the various family lifestyles and backgrounds.

• •

Related Activities

1. Integrate with social studies and literature.
    Divide the class into small groups. Using
    your class heritage tree as a starting guide,
    assign a different country to each group
    (also consider what resources are available).
    Each group should read books (fiction and
    nonfiction) and do research on its country.
    Give each group a list of certain, specified
    information as goals for discovery. The
    groups should find a way to present their
    information to the class via poster, booklet,
    or oral report. In addition they should also
    show a craft or act out a folk story from
    their country. (Note: students should not
    necessarily be assigned to a country based
    on their ancestral origins.)

2. Enjoy books on the lesson topic. Possible
    titles on the resources list.

LESSON 8: DEATH, GRIEF, AND BEYOND

Preparation/Materials
- Student Activity—Sets 1 and 2. Cut apart the numbered statements.
- Optional: glue the statements on cards.
- Personal story, Bible story, or book excerpt about death to introduce topic of death
- Unit Evaluation

Objectives
- Students will understand what death means.
- Students will understand that grief is a fitting response to death as well as to other losses (divorce, moving).
- Students will know the comfort of Christian hope.

Background
In an effort to make children's lives easier, many adults tend to shield them from the reality of death. While well-intentioned, these actually do a disservice to the children. David Peretz, faculty member of Columbia University, describes how over-protective attitudes affect children. "The very young approach life as naturalists, open-minded and curious. Unfortunately, their early experiences with death and the reactions of those around them frequently close down their openness and curiosity, leading to avoidance and denial. A child's first questions about death are an attempt to gain mastery over frightening images of abandonment, separation, loneliness, pain, and bodily damage. If we err on the side of overprotecting them from emotional pain and grief with 'kind' lies, we risk weakening their coping capacities. Children will absorb our defensiveness, avoidance, denial, and general unwillingness to discuss death directly. Death becomes, quite literally, something unspeakable." (Foreword in *How Do We Tell the Children?* by Schaefer and Lyons [Newmarket Press, 1986]).

And so we need to speak of death to our children in order to ease their fears and to increase their abilities to cope, but more importantly to share our conviction that Christ has removed the sting of death. Christ's bodily resurrection is the guarantee of our resurrection. Denying the reality of death, then, is denying our need for Christ.

Some of your students may have a mature understanding of death; others may have a very limited or immature understanding. Their attitudes and ideas will largely depend on their experience and the attitudes of the adults in their lives. As children develop, however, so does their understanding of death. By age 8 or 9 many children recognize that death is irreversible, although they may still have difficulty recognizing that they too will die. Be aware that sometimes children interpret death as a punishment or they fear that death is contagious. In an attempt to gain a sense of control children may act out very violent wars or accidents, complete with gory details.

In her book, *Helping Children Grieve* (Augsburg, 1991), Theresa Huntley offers a few guidelines for talking to children about death. First of all, establish a feeling of trust and open rapport with the children. Answer questions truthfully, but answer only what is being asked. If you are unsure what the child wants to know, you may ask what they think the answer is in order to pinpoint what information they are seeking. Second, encourage the children to show their feelings and assure them that it is okay to feel the way they do. Death is a hard subject. Third, avoid ideas that deny the children's need and lead children to feel angry at God. For example, saying that God took the person or needed that person more than his or her family/friends is inappropriate. Also avoid confusing euphemisms such as "sleeping," "gone away," "lost," and "left us."

Remember that your students are building vocabulary in this area. Encourage students to ask if they don't understand or if they feel confused.

Your students will approach this lesson with a mixture of keen interest and trepidation, of questions and answers, of clear insights and confusion. Some of their questions will have very obvious answers. For other questions there will be no answers—there will only be more questions. As you guide your students in learning about death, offer them the support and comfort of being a child of God. God knows the answers. God will make all things well.

Should your students experience the death of a classmate or of someone they know during the school year, you may need to plan some specific working-it-out activities such as journals, good-bye gifts, or grief counseling. Accept the wide variety of student reactions to death. Remember that grief is experienced and expressed in as many ways and timetables as there are individuals.

Note: *Horizons Health* in grades 3–6 will explore different aspects of death and grieving at each grade level and in more depth than at the early elementary levels. Each grade level will stress the Christian assurance of resurrection.

Grade 3: What it means to be "dead"
Grade 4: The stages of grief
Grade 5: Rituals surrounding death
Grade 6: Helping the dying and those who grieve

Lesson

1. Introduce the topic of death by relating a personal story or reading a book (for possible titles, see Related Activities) or a Bible story (for example, the death of Jacob [Genesis 49:29–50:14] or Lazarus [John 11:1–43]).

2. Discover your students' understanding of death. Give students opportunities to relate their experiences of death or talk about their thoughts about death. Respond to each student's contributions, showing support for each one and modeling Christian caring with comments such as "Oh, that must have been very hard for you," "Were you very close?" "What do you remember about ___?"

   Tell the class that it sounds as if they already know some things about death. Explain that you and they will share what you collectively know to see if you can understand death a little better.

3. Next, ask class members how they feel when they talk about death. Stress that fear, sadness, curiosity, and confusion are all natural and appropriate reactions. Note that adults feel the same way. Point out that knowing a little bit more about something can make it less frightening. Asking questions and talking with friends about death can make the subject less confusing.

4. **Student activity.** Use the two sets of statements for a True/False activity, "To Tell the Truth." Students should come up to the front by pairs. One of the students reads a statement from Set 1. The other student reads the same numbered statement from Set 2. Then the class votes/discusses which of the two statements they believe is true.

(While some of the statements are elementary or obvious, it's good to start on safe, comfortable ground with this sensitive topic.) Place these at an activity center, along with books dealing with death, for the students to look through later.

Note: Although this activity has a game format, maintain an atmosphere of reflection and respect. This should not become a competition. (Be sensitive to the reactions of children who have had a recent or very intimate experience with death. You may want to talk to the parents in advance about the lesson.)

> *Set 1: 1 (false), 2 (false), 3 (false), 4 (false), 5 (true), 6 (true), 7 (true), 8 (true), 9 (false), 10 (false),*
>
> *Set 2: 1 (true), 2 (true), 3 (true), 4 (true) 5 (false), 6 (false), 7 (false), 8 (false), 9 (true), 10 (true)*

5. Continue the discussion by talking about grief. Tell students that people feel a special, deep sadness when someone they know has died. This feeling is called grief. People also feel grief when a pet dies, when they move, or when their family goes through a divorce. Everybody feels grief in a different way because each person is unique.

6. Close by restating your positive, Christian perspective on death. Give students the assurance that because Christ became alive again, we know that we will also. Stress that all who believe in Christ have new life, a kind of life that is eternal. Christians grieve, but Christians also have hope that comes from knowing we will be with our loved ones again.

7. **Unit evaluation.** Use the worksheet to review and evaluate. Answers will vary for all of the worksheet questions.

• •

Related Activities

1. Give students the opportunity to write in their journals about their own experiences with grief due to death, lost friendships, or divorce. Or have them write or draw about what they think heaven is like.

2. Have students ask their parents what they think heaven is like. Perhaps suggest that together they read Revelation 21:1–4. The next day ask students to write a paragraph about heaven and then illustrate their work.

3. Sing appropriate songs about Christ's resurrection or the comfort of Christian hope (also cited at grade 2). Suggested songs: "Children of the Heavenly Father" (*Psalter Hymnal,* 440; *Songs of God's Love,* 62); "He's Got the Whole World in His Hands" (*Songs of God's Love,* 56); "The Lord's My Shepherd" (*Proclaim Songbook 2,* 16; *Psalter Hymnal,* 161; alternate tune, *Children's Hymnbook,* 19); "Christ the Lord Is Risen Today" (*Psalter Hymnal,* 388); "I Will Sing of the Mercies of the Lord" (*Psalter Hymnal,* 169)

4. At an activity center provide books dealing with death and with grief and loss due to moving, a pet's death, or divorce. Read at least one of the books on this theme to the class. Use the resouces list for some options.

Being on the Safe Side

Goals

- Students will be alert to hazards and behaviors that threaten safety.
- Students will decide to act safely to protect themselves and others.

Background

Health education helps students fulfill their God-given task of caring for creation, a task that includes being caretakers of themselves. This unit promotes awareness of the safety and health choices that students make daily. It stresses the importance of taking responsibility for these choices and of taking precautions in order to avoid injury and harm to self and to others.

This unit deals with several sensitive safety issues. One is the issue of sexual abuse. As much as we would like children to remain innocent, in order to protect them we must deal with the reality of sinful acts such as child abuse. We are doing our students a disservice if we ignore the topic or cover it only superficially. Children need to be prepared to protect themselves from abuse, and children who are being abused must be offered the opportunity to reach out for help and healing.

Another sensitive unit issue is HIV/AIDS—acquired immune deficiency syndrome. In kindergarten through grade 2, HIV/AIDS is not specifically addressed, but students learn about wellness behaviors that reduce the risk of infection. In grade 3 HIV/AIDS is identified as a communicable disease caused by a virus and spread through body fluids. Lessons in higher grades build on this information so that students receive HIV/AIDS education in developmentally appropriate ways.

Because HIV/AIDS receives wide attention in the media, students in grade 3 are probably aware of HIV/AIDS and may raise questions about it. Teachers must be prepared to answer their questions with age-appropriate information. The United States Department of Health and Human Services' *Guidelines for Effective School Health Education to Prevent the Spread of AIDS* (MMWR Supplement, January 29, 1988) suggests that education about HIV/AIDS for students in early elementary grades should center on allaying excessive fears and consist of these three concepts:

- HIV/AIDS is a disease that is causing some adults to get very sick, but AIDS does not commonly affect children.
- HIV/AIDS is very hard to get. You cannot get it just by being near or touching someone who has it.
- Scientists all over the world are working hard to find a way to stop people from getting HIV/AIDS and to cure those who have it.

Vocabulary

Integrate the following vocabulary:

reflectors	refrigerate	handlebars	brakes	HIV/AIDS	bicycling
risk/risky	accident	lifeguard	labels	virus	chain/chain guard
carelessness	electricity	sexual abuse	injury	scrape	electric shock
chronic	bacteria	poisons	blister	plug	poisonous plants
emergency	wound	first aid	private	sparks	electric appliance
diseases	vaccine	tricked	toxins	bicycle	communicable

Unit Resources (Search online for similar resources if these are no longer available)

Davis, Diane. *Something Is Wrong at My House: A Book About Parent Fighting*. Seattle: Parenting Press, 1984.

> The topic of domestic violence is not covered in the health program, but teachers may find this a helpful one-on-one resource to use with students living with family violence.
> A phone application that allows students to practice dialing emergency numbers is available by visiting https://www.coolkidsfirstaid.com/.

Information on Safety in the Home & Community for Parents with Children (Ages 4-11).
> Centers for Disease Control and Prevention.
> https://www.cdc.gov/parents/children/safety.html/.
> Contains a lengthy list of topics with information on each area of safety.

Safety for All Seasons. Nationwide Children's Hospital, 2010.
> Activity book about safety: cars, playgrounds, crossing the street, etc. Color pages and puzzles. Free to download by visiting NationwideChildrens.org/Safety.

Child Abuse and Neglect Prevention. Centers for Disease Control and Prevention.
> https://www.cdc.gov/violenceprevention/childabuseandneglect/index.html.
> This web page provides a short video, links to more detailed information, and a downloadable pdf.

Lesson Resources (Search online for similar resources if these are no longer available)

Lesson 2

"Water Safety for Kids. Red Cross."
> Videos and activities for Grade K-2 and 3-6.

Lesson 5

There are two lesson plans on safety available on scholastic.com: *Safety Savvy* and *Be a Safety Sleuth*. Both are easy to follow, suitable for grades 3-4, and includes links and printables.

"Learn Not to Burn. Sparky School House."
> Curriculum materials are posted on this page up to grade 2, but the free grade 2 materials can be adapted to suit other ages. Informative videos are also available.

Lesson 6

"Play it Safe: Prevent Facial Injuries With Simple Sports Safety Precautions."
> American Dental Association, 2013.

The Red Cross provides online and in-person first aid training.

Lesson 7

"Resources for Kids." Childhelp.
> The page of the website provides a list of things kids should know and a suggested book list.

Girard, Linda Walvoord. *My Body Is Private.* Niles, Ill.: Whitman, 1984.
  Sensitively written book covering types of touches, how to deal with disturbing situations, and telling adults about inappropriate touch. Ages 5–8.

Gordon, Sol and Judith. *A Better Safe Than Sorry Book.* Fayetteville, N.Y.: Ed-U-Press, 1984.
  A read-aloud book aimed at children ages 3–9, which provides essential information about sexual assault. Shows parents believing children, respecting them, and giving good touches. Names anatomical parts and gives several drawings of nude children.

Kraizer, Sherryll Kerns. *The Safe Child Book.* New York: Delacorte, 1985.
  This book is intended for parents, but teachers will also find it helpful because of its concrete approach to preventing sexual abuse of children.

Prevent Child Sexual Abuse: Facts about sexual abuse and how to prevent it.
  Stop It Now!, 2020.
  This pdf provides details information and resources. More information (printable and topic-specific) can be found on stopitnow.org.

Sanford, Doris. *I Can't Talk About It.* Portland, Ore.: Multnomah Press, 1986.
  Annie, a child who is being sexually abused by her father, talks with God about her pain. Two noteworthy aspects: its sensitivity to abused children's tendency to blame themselves and its stress on the need for forgiveness. Not suitable to read in its entirety in the classroom, but the book may be helpful for approaching a child who has been abused.

Lessons 8 and 9

"Healthy Hygiene with Kids." Alliance for Consumer Education.
  https://www.consumered.org/healthy-hygiene-with-kids.
  The website contains videos and lesson plans that focus on hand washing.

"HIV/AIDS Facts & Worksheets." Kidskonnect. https://kidskonnect.com/science/hiv-aids/.
  Free downloadable worksheets and some review information.

LESSON 1: ACCIDENTS AND RISK-TAKING

Preparation/Materials
- Student Activity
- Student books

Objectives
- Students will identify the connection between accidents and taking unsafe risks.
- Students will become aware of specific unsafe risks they take.
- Students will recognize their responsibility for helping to prevent accidents.

Background
Accidents are the leading cause of death among elementary school children. What types of accidents? Car accidents, falls, fires, and drownings are the most common. And for young children poisoning is also a serious threat. Most of these accidents occur because of carelessness, but some occur because of ignorance (for example, being unaware of the danger of swimming during a thunderstorm).

This opening unit lesson focuses on human carelessness as a cause of accidents. It makes students aware of the connection between hurried and unthinking behavior and accidents. This is an important point to make. Most likely many students think the word accident means "not my fault."

This lesson is a good time to discuss the Christian perspective on safety, to stress that acting in a safe and responsible manner is one way to honor God. Of course, we believe that our ultimate safety is in God's hand, but that does not excuse Christians from taking responsibility for their actions and from learning about potential safety hazards and how to avoid them.

• •

Lesson
1. Introduce the lesson by telling about an accident you had that was caused by carelessness or by asking students to tell about accidents.

2. Pick up on incidents described in Step 1 and discuss the connection between risky behavior and accidents. Explain that although life is full of risks, we can help to prevent accidents by avoiding unnecessary or unsafe risks. Give illustrations from everyday life (for example, normal risk and unsafe risk connected with boating, swimming, bike riding, and other activities). Write the words *risky action* on the board.

   Write the word *hazard* on the board. Discuss what a hazard is. Ask students to name possible hazards children might encounter as they engage in the everyday activities just mentioned. During the discussion draw an arrow from the words *risky action* to *hazard* to illustrate how this combination can cause accidents.

   risky action ⟶ hazard ⟶ ACCIDENT

3. **Student book.** Have students turn to "Safe Kids Are No Accident" in their student books. Read the letter to all the king's horses and all the king's men from Humpty Dumpty who is in the hospital following his legendary fall from the wall. Discuss the "Think It Over" questions.

   1. *Lead students to understand that acting in a safe and responsible way shows that we appreciate the life God gave us.*
   2. *Students acting in an unsafe way may bring injury/accident to others. "Love your neighbor" has implications here.*
   3. *Answers will vary. Include knowing about safety, being aware of hazards, choosing to follow safety rules.*
   4. *Discuss dares and how they create peer pressure to do unsafe things.*

4. Ask students to identify other unsafe behaviors and hazards that could combine to cause accidents. Or call out unsafe behavior and have students name possible hazards that might cause an accident/injury (walking barefoot along the side of a road, jumping into swimming pool or lake without a safety check, running after a ball that rolls into the road, not wearing a seatbelt on a short ride to the store, stepping out of a parked car on the road side instead of the curb side, climbing around on a construction site when no one's there).

5. **Student activity.** Use the activity sheet to help class members recognize how often their behavior is risky. After students have filled in the boxes, discuss the hazard listed. Since family rules will vary widely, provide ample opportunity to discuss why a behavior is or is not allowed.

6. Close by summarizing the lesson.

• •

Related Activities

1. Ask the school nurse or principal to identify the most common kinds of accidents at school. Together discuss what can be done (or what has been done) to prevent the most common kinds of accidents.

2. Assign students to keep a "Safety Snoop" log. Have them be safety detectives recording their observations in the log. Make this a one- or two-day log, or continue the activity throughout the unit. Share the results. Are there any patterns the class can discern?

LESSON 2: BICYCLE SAFETY

Preparation/Materials

- Student books
- Optional: Contact AAA or local police department for brochures on bicycle safety.

Objectives

- Students will identify causes of bicycle accidents.
- Students will list safety rules for bicycle drivers.

Background

Since many students in grade 3 are beginning to bike further away from home, they need to be alerted to hazards of biking. Stress that bicyclists must "go with the flow" of traffic and are expected to follow traffic rules.

Although this lesson centers on bicycle safety, we suggest that teachers be aware of new play fads or equipment and the possible safety hazards they present, adding safety instruction as necessary. The proverbial "ounce of prevention" is the rule here.

• •

Lesson

1. Introduce the lesson by asking how many class members (or their family members) have had bicycle accidents. Explain that this lesson will help students be safe bicycle riders.

2. Discuss the main causes of bicycle accidents. Work as a class to develop a list of causes, or have groups of students work together to make lists and then compare them. Some causes to include:
   - improperly maintained bike (malfunctioning brakes or horn, no reflectors or light for night riding)
   - road hazards (potholes, loose gravel, patches of mud, leaves, soft shoulders)
   - parked car problem
   - turning vehicles
   - bicycle "ride-outs"(riding into the roadway from driveways or from between parked cars without looking)
   - bad weather conditions (rain, ice patches)
   - not yielding to pedestrians
   - not obeying traffic regulations, signs, and signals
   - not signaling intended actions

3. **Student book.** Direct the class to the student book section entitled "Wanted: Expert Drivers." Note that students have pinpointed some causes of bicycle accidents; now they are going to learn ways to avoid accidents and stay safe when they are riding bicycles.

Read or assign students to read "Wanted: Expert Drivers." Talk about the term "bicycle driver," pointing out that it stresses that the person on the bicycle is responsible for operating it, not just riding it. Incorporate the "Think It Over" questions.

1. *Ask an adult to help them check the bike. You may wish to identify specific parts to check, such as brakes and tires. Bikes should also have a chain guard, reflectors, and working bell and light. Elicit the importance of each item from the class.*
2. *Ask students to enumerate rules listed in the student book. Stress that drivers need to know what bicycle drivers are going to do.*
3. *Answers will vary. Lead students to realize they jeopardize others' safety when they don't follow traffic/safety rules.*

Discussion suggestions:
- For the first rule, talk about what a safe bicycle is. Note that the bicycle should be the correct size. Elicit from students the way to tell whether a bike is the right size (when sitting on the seat, the driver should be able to place the ball of his or her foot on the ground, without tipping the bicycle). Then discuss the parts of the bike that should be in working condition: brakes, chain guard, tires, and horn. The bike should also be equipped with reflectors and a light. If time permits, talk about the importance of each item.
- Since ride-outs are one of the chief causes of serious bike accidents, spend time explaining what a ride-out is and why it is dangerous. Consider having several students role-play a ride-out to demonstrate the danger.

Study the pictures of hand signals and then give students the opportunity to practice them. Call out "left turn," "right turn," or "stop," and have students respond with the correct signal.

4. Summarize the lesson. Refer to the list of accident causes composed in Step 2. Stress that many accidents can be avoided by being aware of hazards and avoiding them.

5. Optional: To reinforce lesson concepts distribute brochures on bike safety for students to take home and read with parents.

Related Activities

1. Arrange with the local police department for a bike inspection at school.

2. Have students make a bicycle inspection checklist, and have each student take it home to complete. If students themselves don't own bikes, they can check the bike of an older sibling or family friend.

3. Have groups of students role-play a variety of situations and have the rest of the class decide whether or not the bicyclist drove safely.

4. Show a film about bicycle safety to reinforce lesson concepts. See Unit Resources for suggestions.

LESSON 3: BASIC WATER SAFETY

Preparation/Materials
- Student Activity
- Student books

Objectives
- Students will know basic rules for swimming safely.
- Students will understand the reasons for the rules.

Background
The U.S. National Safety Council reports that although in recent years drownings in the United States were reduced from 10.4 drownings per 100,000 people to fewer than 3.0 drownings per 100,000, in 1986 drownings increased by 6 percent. The increase was mainly due to home drownings. Another sobering fact is this: drowning is one of the leading causes of death for children.

Raising awareness about water safety in school is one way to help reduce drownings. Of course, there is no safety substitute for knowing how to swim before playing around water. Be sure to stress this during the lesson. Encourage class members to take swimming lessons and learn how to be good swimmers—both for fun and safety.

• •

Lesson

1. Ask students to close their eyes and recall the last time they went swimming. Tell them to picture the place where they swam, the people with whom they went, the weather, and the temperature of the water. Then ask them to call out words describing the experience.

2. Next, ask students to recall family swimming rules. Tell them that their books have rules for smart swimmers, too.

3. **Student book.** Read the student book section "Smart Swimmers" together. Discuss each safety rule as it is read, asking students to identify why the rule is necessary. Note when rules similar to family rules are read. Answer the "Think It Over" questions.

    1. *Swimming with a buddy helps keep you and others safe. Staying away from diving boards and slides helps to prevent a collision with another swimmer/diver. Avoiding rough play helps keep all swimmers safe.*
    2. *Get out of water during thunderstorms. Lightning travels through water, and electric shock is a danger.*

4. Ask the class to name other ways to stay safe around water (include boating safety). Additional safety rules: calling for help only in a real emergency, not chewing gum while swimming, wearing a life jacket in a boat, holding onto an overturned boat until help comes, getting out of the water when there is thunder or lightning.

5. **Student activity.** Review safety rules with the crossword puzzle activity. Students should first fill in the sentence blanks and then match numbers to complete the crossword puzzle.

   a. *7–under, 8–diving*
   b. *10–buddy*
   c. *9 down–swimming*
   d. *4–place*
   e. *2–lifeguard, 13–duty*
   f. *3–well*
   g. *11–tired, 1–cold*
   h. *5–deep*
   i. *6–pushing, 12–running*
   j. *9 across–safe*

   As you go over the completed puzzle with the class, stress the importance of preventing accidents around water by thinking about consequences before acting.

• •

Related Activities

1. Have a Red Cross representative talk to the students about water safety.

2. Integrate with language arts and have students write stories about the scene they imagined in Step 1 of the lesson.

3. Student volunteers can make a comprehensive list of water-safety rules to post in the classroom.

4. Tell the fable of the boy who cried wolf for the fun of it just once too often. Tie in with the danger of pretending to drown. Students should never call for help in the water unless help is needed.

LESSON 4: A SHOCKING LESSON

Preparation/Materials
- Student Activity
- Student books

Objective
- Students will identify safe/unsafe ways to handle electrical appliances.

Background

North Americans are surrounded by electrical appliances, and because of stringent manufacturing codes most of these appliances are safe to use. Still, users must learn to respect the power of electricity and follow basic safety rules. A plugged-in radio, for example, can elec-trocute a bather if it falls into the bath water. And damaged electrical cords can emit sparks and cause fire.

Developing safety awareness about handling electric appliances is important for children in grade 3. Small children are usually warned to stay away from electrical outlets and appliances, but some children in grade 3 are becoming more independent and are beginning to handle simple appliances on their own. Nonetheless, many children are ignorant of the dangers connected with electricity and electrical appliances. Knowing about specific dangers will do much to "shock proof" them.

Lesson

1. Open the lesson by asking students to imagine what life would be like without electricity. Have them share their ideas and talk about what a wonderful gift electricity is.

   Then ask if they think electricity is dangerous and elicit from the class the danger of fires, shocks, and burns from electricity. Briefly tell of an accident you or one of your family members had with an electric appliance or give students an opportunity to tell about such experiences. Explain that today's lesson will be about preventing accidents caused by electrical appliances, wires, or outlets.

   Teach new vocabulary as necessary.

2. **Student book.** Read and discuss the section entitled "Electric Whiz" in the student book.

   Elicit from students the correct way to get stuck toast out of a toaster (turn off if possible, unplug, and ask for adult help). Explain or elicit from students that electric current runs from the outlet, along the cord, to the appliance. Answer the "Think It Over" questions.

   1. *Answers will vary.*
   2. *Unplug an electric appliance such as a toaster before working with it; always pull on the plug and not on the cord to unplug an appliance; don't touch radio or other small appliance with wet hands.*

3. After discussing material in the student book, talk about outside electrical hazards that children should be aware of. Explain the danger of trying to get a kite out of power lines (or of rescuing a cat perched on lines) or of using a long rake or other object to try to poke at power lines. Also cover the importance of staying away from electric wires downed by storms or accidents.

4. **Student activity.** Have students find the electrical hazards in the picture. Complete the activity as a class, or have students work individually or in pairs to find the hazards and then discuss findings with the class. Tell students to be prepared to explain why the pictured hazards are unsafe and to describe safe behavior.

   Puzzle answers:
   1. *Small child playing with electric socket.*
   2. *Frayed electric cord that could cause fire.*
   3. *Electric cord running under rug.*
   4. *Trying to undo kite that is caught in power lines.*
   5. *Climbing tree near power lines.*
   6. *Washing an electrical appliance while it's still plugged in.*
   7. *Repairing toaster while it's still plugged in.*
   8. *Overloading an outlet with too many cords.*
   9. *Curtains blowing against lamp.*
   10. *Sloppy bandage repair to broken electric cord.*

• •

Related Activities

1. Integrate with language arts and art—and stimulate creativity—by having students create an electrical appliance. Students can draw the creations and write about what the appliance can do. Suggestions to get students started: student desk with a miniature built-in microwave for heating up lunch (handy for leftover pizza), an electric pencil that lights up when a writer makes a spelling error.

2. Tell or read the story of Benjamin Franklin flying his kite during a thunderstorm. Discuss the danger of this experiment.

LESSON 5: REVIEW OF BASIC SAFETY PRACTICES

Preparation/Materials
- Student Activity
- Optional: chart paper

Objectives
- Students will be able to identify unsafe behavior (pedestrian, car/seatbelt, etc.).
- Students will identify various community workers who help to prevent accidents.

Lesson

1. Divide the class into groups and assign each group a safety topic. Direct each group to think of and list as many safety rules for their topic as they can. Pick topics not covered in previous unit lessons: pedestrian safety; school bus safety; playground safety; safety at home; fire safety; basic stranger education (preventing sexual abuse covered in Lesson 7).

   Go over the rules in a full class session. Add important rules that were omitted. Write the rules on chart paper, and display them in the classroom.

2. Discuss the role of community workers in safety. Ask: "How do people in the community help keep us safe?" Include the following: keeping streets safer by removing leaves or dirt and gravel from the side of roads; in winter, removing ice and snow from streets; painting markings on the road for drivers to follow; putting up traffic signs and lights to regulate traffic; putting fences around construction areas; maintaining a fire department for putting out fires.

3. **Student activity.** Use the activity to reinforce basic safety concepts. Have students complete the first two sample rhymes by filling in the blanks (car, space). Then ask them to complete the rest of the rhymes by making up a second line for each. Students may enjoy working on this activity with a partner. If time permits, have them make up their own safety rhymes. The last section encourages the class to think about how the school and their families help them to be safe. As class members share their answers, stress again each individual's responsibility for safety (for example, the school can provide crossing guards, but students must be willing to obey/respect them).

Related Activities

1. Have students check and count home fire protection devices. How many have smoke detectors and/or fire extinguishers?

2. Bring a smoke detector to class and let students hear what the alarm sounds like.

3. Use materials listed under Lesson 5 Resources to review or reteach basic safety rules.

LESSON 6: HELPING IN AN EMERGENCY / FIRST AID

Preparation/Materials
- Student books
- Optional: props such as toy telephones, bandages, washcloths for role-plays

Objectives
- Students will review steps to follow in emergencies.
- Students will identify simple first-aid procedures.

Background

This lesson begins with a review of emergency procedures. Although earlier grade levels have covered steps to follow in an emergency, periodically reviewing the material ensures that students are prepared to act quickly and decisively.

This lesson also introduces students to basic first aid for minor scrapes, cuts, and nosebleeds. It also explains proper procedure if a permanent tooth is knocked out. According to the American Dental Association, there are annually over 25,000 school accidents involving injury to the face and mouth that require the assistance of a school employee. The American Dental Association stresses that if a tooth is knocked out, it should not be cleaned. The tooth should be wrapped in a wet cloth or placed in water or milk and taken immediately with the child to a dentist (within an hour, if possible).

● ●

Lesson

1. Write the word *emergency* on the board, and ask students what an emergency is. Explain that this lesson will help them know what to do in an emergency.

2. **Student book.** Assign students to read "Action Plan" under the section "Are You Ready to Handle an Emergency?" in the student book. Have class members tell what steps to follow in an emergency. Discuss each step. Stress giving clear information when reporting an emergency. You may wish to suggest that they use a who, where, what sequence for reporting. (Because clearly stating *where* can be difficult for children, give students practice in describing various locations.) If they are on the phone, also emphasize the importance of paying close attention to any directions given and of not hanging up until they are told to or until the other person hangs up. To reinforce the steps, consider having a volunteer write them on the board as students say or read them.

   Read and discuss the section "First-Aid Facts" from the student book. In discussing minor injuries, stress the importance of reporting them to an adult. Emphasize that *any* injury should be reported to an adult. Also make sure children understand that if a cut or scrape bleeds a lot, it isn't a small cut, and they should get help right away. The wound may be deep. Suggest applying firm pressure on the wound to help stop the bleeding while they are getting help.

As you talk about what to do if a tooth is knocked out, also review ways to prevent accidents to teeth. (Observe safety rules when playing games and using drinking fountains. Those engaged in contact sports should wear mouth protectors.)

Answer the "Think It Over" questions.

1. *A first-aid kit is a box or bag with medicines, bandages, and other things for treating injuries. A kit is especially important to have when we are camping or hiking, when we can't easily get medical help.*
2. *Cuts and scrapes should be washed with soap and water. Use adhesive bandages if necessary. Mild burns should be held under cold water. Blisters may feel better with adhesive bandages over them. If blisters break, wash the area and apply an adhesive bandage.*
3. *Sit down, lean forward, pinch nose closed, and stay in position for 5 to 10 minutes. If bleeding doesn't stop, an adult should contact a doctor.*
4. *Find the tooth and wrap it in a clean, wet cloth or put it in a glass of water or milk. Don't try to clean the tooth. Quickly tell an adult and get to a dentist for treatment.*

3. Have students role-play situations showing how to deal with emergencies and minor injuries covered in the lesson. Divide the class into small groups. Have each group work together to develop one situation to present to the rest of the class.

● ●

Related Activities

1. Invite the school nurse or a Red Cross representative to speak to the class about first-aid techniques.

2. Have interested students read about other first-aid measures and report their findings to the rest of the class.

3. Give students the opportunity to practice making calls to report emergencies.

4. Volunteers may wish to research the various kinds of accidental injuries to bones and muscles and report findings to the rest of the class. Or have small groups research a type of bone break or bone or muscle injury (greenstick break, open, closed or multiple fracture, dislocated bone, sprain or strain). Members could divide responsibilities: some researching, some writing, and some drawing illustrations.

LESSON 7: PREVENTING SEXUAL ABUSE

Preparation/Materials
- Become familiar with topic through appropriate teacher resources.
- Teacher Visual

Objectives
- Students will learn self-protection skills.
- Students will understand that trickery is often involved in sexual abuse.
- Students will choose to use good touches to encourage class members.

Background
Some may question the need for child-abuse education in Christian schools, but reliable research has shown that abuse does occur in Christian families and communities. And the rate of abuse is comparable to or only a little lower than that of the population as a whole. So although we may wish to believe that the problem does not exist in Christian communities, the facts do not support that view. Christian communities need to face the reality of abuse and help students develop skills for dealing with it.

Each grade level of *Horizons Health* addresses the problem of sexual abuse. Since this is a sensitive subject, it is important for the school to contact parents/caregivers in advance and inform them of lesson content. You may wish to do this by letter or by meeting with parents (or your school administrator may prefer to hold a meeting to which parents of all grades are invited). Good communication with the home will give parents the opportunity to work with the school and to reinforce safety concepts.

The central focus of this lesson is safety, not sex education. In this unit students have been learning about safety—traffic safety, fire safety, home safety, bicycle safety. Now they are learning about one more type of safety—safety from sexual assault. (There are communities that do not have sex education programs but that *do* teach prevention of sexual abuse.) Students who are aware of the danger of sexual abuse and know how to protect themselves are less likely to become victims of sexual abuse.

To be effective, sexual abuse prevention education must cover the following basic areas in age-appropriate ways: (1) recognizing sexual abuse/differentiating between appropriate and inappropriate touch, (2) learning self-protection skills and techniques, and (3) identifying resources for help. We want to emphasize that presenting information on the subject of sexual abuse is not sufficient. Students also need to develop skills—decision-making skills and self-assertive protection skills. They must not only understand what inappropriate touch is, but must also understand what they can do about inappropriate touch.

It's also vital to present the material a non-threatening way. Introduce the topic of touch in a way that makes you and the class feel comfortable. Having the classroom teacher present the material is preferable, but if you are unable to teach the lesson comfortably, consider asking another qualified person to teach it, perhaps another teacher on the school staff. This is an important safety lesson, and it should be presented in a supportive environment.

As you teach the lesson, be clear and direct; use correct names when referring to body parts. If a child should begin to report abuse during class (an unlikely event), offer to talk with him or her later and follow the protocol established by your school for reporting child abuse.

Lesson

1. Deal with students' embarrassment by stating that the topic of this lesson, touching, can be an embarrassing topic to talk about, but it is an important safety topic. Understanding the difference between kinds of touches and knowing what to do about certain touches is important for keeping ourselves safe—just as important as knowing about water safety or fire safety.

   Create a climate conducive to open communication. Make clear that each student will be expected to respect the questions and comments of other class members during the discussion. Also encourage students to actively participate from the beginning of the lesson.

2. Review the concept of good and bad touch. Ask students to identify some good touches (loving hug from family member, goodnight kiss from parent, friendly pat of neighbor) and bad touches (kick, shove, punch, scratch). Explain that some touches that may be good in some circumstances may make us uncomfortable in others (tickling that doesn't stop, too-tight hugs, kiss on the lips from aunt or uncle). Some of these touches may confuse us. Even though we can't explain why we don't like them, somehow we have an "uh-oh" or "no" feeling about the touch.

3. Use the visual to introduce the topic of inappropriate touching of private body parts. Review the fact that God made all parts of our bodies good, but some parts are private. Identify (or ask students to identify) which parts of the body are private: parts covered by a bathing suit or underwear. If approved by school policy, teach correct anatomical terms for private body parts (breast, vulva, vagina, penis, scrotum, testicles, anus, buttocks) using the visual from Unit 3, Lesson 2.

   Ask students to identify situations in which adults have good reason to touch the private parts of the body (doctors and nurses for medical reasons; parents for medical or hygienic reasons).

4. Explain that someone's touching the private parts of a child's body by force or trickery is called sexual abuse. Write the words *sexual abuse* on the board. Explain that in sexual abuse sometimes a person will also force or trick a child into touching the adult's private parts. Emphasize that abuse is never the child's fault; it is always the fault of the adult or older person.

5. Elicit from class members suggestions for self-protection if someone touches them in a way that is uncomfortable, embarrassing, or wrong. In the discussion include the following actions: saying no in a clear and confident way, moving away or getting away from the person, and telling a trusted adult about the touch. Stress that if students have an "uh-oh" or "no" feeling about the touch, they should trust that feeling and act on it to protect themselves.

Discuss the following questions:
- What if the first adult they tell doesn't believe them? (Tell another adult. Keep telling until someone believes him or her.)
- What if the abuser makes the child promise to keep the touching a secret? (It's not fair for adults or older children to pressure a child to keep a secret that is scary or disturbing. These kinds of secrets are intended to hide things that shouldn't be hidden. The child should tell even if he or she has promised not to. Sometimes a child may have to promise not to tell in order to get away.)
- What are some examples of good secrets? (Birthday gifts or surprise parties.) Bad secrets? (Sibling's shoplifting, school friend's vandalizing, and touching that is wrong or makes them feel uncomfortable or unhappy.)
- Who are some adults that children could tell about sexual abuse? (Teacher, family members, pastor, school counselor, neighbor or other adult friend, police.)

6. Focus on the trickery that is often part of sexual abuse. Give a personal example of how someone tricked you into doing something (not touching). Ask students why the person used a trick (most likely to get you to do something you would not have wanted to do). Note that people trick others into wrong or uncomfortable touching for the same reason.

7. Use some "what if" situations to help students identify potentially dangerous situations, and consider ways to realistically deal with them. Include situations involving both strangers and adults familiar to the child. (Remember that according to statistics only about 10 percent of child sexual abuse incidents involve strangers.) Take the time to develop one or two of these situations in some detail. Stop the story to ask students to comment on how the child may be feeling and what he or she can do. Tell the stories in the third person; avoid using names of class members.

Examples of situations:
- a friendly stranger asking Sal to help him or her find a lost car key, pet, or child
- a grown-up uncle/older cousin coming into the bathroom while child is taking a bath
- a camp counselor or older camper showing pornographic pictures and undressing in front of child

Example of developed "what if" situation and discussion:

Uncle Pete often babysits at Amy's house. He and Amy have lots of good times together. One night when Uncle Pete is babysitting, he offers to read Amy a story. He pulls her onto his lap. But this time after he finishes the story, he puts his hand on the top part of her leg, her thigh, and then between her legs on her private parts. He tells her to keep the touching a secret. He tells Amy that she's old enough to have a special secret with him. Then he promises to buy her a new toy. (At this point ask students how they think Amy might feel, and add your own suggestions: disappointed, sad, angry, scared, unhappy. Ask: "What can Amy do?" In the discussion include looking directly at Uncle Pete, saying no, and moving away. Then tell students the rest of the story.)

Amy tells Uncle Pete, "No, don't touch me like that. And don't buy me a new toy." Then she gets off Uncle Pete's lap. Later, after her parents come home, she tells them about what happened. Her father says, "I'm glad you told us about it. It's not your fault that Uncle Pete touched your private parts. Uncle Pete won't be your babysitter again, and we'll make sure he doesn't do that again." (Follow up by asking: "Why do you think Uncle Pete offered to buy Amy a new toy? Do you think it was easy or hard for Amy to tell her parents about the touching? Why?" Help them understand that even though it's hard to tell, bad touching is not a good secret to keep.)

8. Use one or more of the following activities to end the lesson in a positive way:

    *   Play "I'm Going on a Trip and I'm Taking a Hug." Have students sit in a circle. Each child in a group adds one expression to what the previous is bringing on the trip: "I'm going on a trip and I'm taking a hug and a handshake and a pat on the back." The last child in the circle receives everything that the rest of the children are taking on the trip. This exercise provides a safe way for children to touch. If children are embarrassed by touching and affection, save this exercise for a time when a sense of community has developed. (Adapted from *The Friendly Classroom for a Small Planet* by Priscilla Prutzman and others [New Society Publishers, 1988.])

    *   Have a "car wash" to accent good touches. Have students (the whole class or a part of the class) create a car wash by lining up in two parallel lines only a few feet apart. Then one student "car" at a time walks through the "wash." Everyone in the lines gives him or her a friendly touch (pat on the back or shoulder, handshake) and makes an encouraging and affectionate remark. The result is a sparkling "car" at the end of the wash. (Adapted from *100 Ways to Enhance Self-Concept in the Classroom* by Canfield and Wells [Prentice Hall, 1976].)

    *   Sing a song about God's guidance and loving care, for example, "What a Friend We Have in Jesus." Talk about God's faithful and constant love, and assure students that when we talk to God about our problems, God hears us.

Related Activities

1. Expand on Step 5 of the lesson. Have students role-play being tricked into doing something (not touching). Ask how they felt about being tricked. What they could do when they found out they had been tricked? Read stories about being tricked (*Aesop's Fables* are a good source) or tell Bible stories about trickery (for example: Delilah tricking Samson, Jacob tricking Esau and Isaac to get the birthright, Laban tricking Jacob). Elicit from students reasons why a person would use trickery in sexual abuse.

2. Define and discuss bribery. Again, use role-plays as a teaching strategy.

3. Use the resources list to expand the lesson.

LESSON 8: COMMUNICABLE AND NONCOMMUNICABLE DISEASES

Preparation/Materials
- Student Activity
- Optional: Obtain pamphlets on communicable and noncommunicable diseases (a list can be found through https://www.alpha.org/).

Objectives
- Students will identify three factors that affect body systems.
- Students will distinguish communicable and noncommunicable diseases.

Background

By grade 3, students are aware that germs make us sick. In the grade 2 students learned that bacteria and viruses are two kinds of germs, that the body has ways to keep out germs (tiny hairs in the nose, skin, wetness in mouth and throat), and that white cells and antibodies can fight germs inside the body.

This and the next lesson focus on "being on the safe side" by having shots and taking measures to prevent the spread of communicable diseases. Explain that by doing these things, we are protecting not only our own health but also the health of others.

Teaching about HIV/AIDS may be controversial in your school community. How much detail you include on HIV/AIDS in this and the next lesson will be determined by your school's educational policy. A balanced approach to the subject bears in mind both the students' need to be alerted to the danger of HIV/AIDS and their need to be reassured that HIV/AIDS is not contracted through casual contact.

As you teach these lessons, help students to gain a Christian perspective on disease and suffering. Help them to understand that disease is part of the brokenness of the world and that life on the new earth will be free from disease and suffering.

(This lesson has been adapted from *Growing Healthy*. [National Center for Health Education, 1975].)

• •

Lesson

1. Brainstorm names of diseases. Write the names on the board as they are suggested. Write the names of communicable diseases on one list and the names of noncommunicable diseases on another. If students don't name any noncommunicable diseases, suggest and write down several with which students may be familiar or see the list below for ideas. As each disease is named and written down, briefly identify symptoms or effects.

   Suggestions for communicable diseases to list:
   - chicken pox
   - measles
   - mumps
   - colds or flu
   - polio
   - mono (mononucleosis)
   - TB (tuberculosis)

- strep throat
- pneumonia
- AIDS (acquired immune deficiency syndrome)

Suggestions for noncommunicable diseases to mention:
- arthritis—attacks joints of skeletal system; joints swell and hurt
- high blood pressure—affects circulatory system; makes heart work harder
- MS (multiple sclerosis)—affects the nervous system; can cause double vision, numbness, and jerky movements of limbs
- MD (muscular dystrophy)—attacks muscular system; weakens muscles that hold bones together affecting posture and movement
- emphysema or asthma—affects respiratory system; disturbs breathing
- ulcers—affects digestive system; causes pain in stomach after eating
- cancer—different types affect different parts of the body

2. Tell students that you have made two lists because diseases fall into two main groups. See if students can figure out how you have classified the diseases. If not, explain that people can "catch" the diseases in one group but not the diseases in the second group. Elicit from students which list names diseases they can catch. Then teach the words *communicable* and *noncommunicable,* and write the appropriate word at the head of each list.

3. Ask: "Why do you think we can catch some diseases and not others?" Explain that communicable diseases are caused by some kinds of germs. Review the fact that two kinds of germs that can cause communicable diseases are bacteria and viruses. Explain that noncommunicable diseases have a variety of causes. They may, for example, be caused by poor diet (a factor in high blood pressure), wear on parts of the body as people get older (some kinds of arthritis), hazards in the environment (smoking and lung cancer), heredity (asthma), and stress (ulcers).

   This is a good opportunity to explain that HIV/AIDS is a communicable disease caused by a virus. It is a disease people can catch, but it's not easy to catch HIV/AIDS. Stress that a person can't catch HIV/AIDS through casual contact with someone who has HIV/AIDS (for example, you can't catch it by being near or touching a person with AIDS, by sharing utensils, etc.). As yet there is no medicine that can cure HIV/AIDS.

4. **Student activity.** Assign students to interview 3–5 adults (parents, grandparents, other relatives, or family friends) to find out names of some illnesses the adults have had. Distribute interview checklists. Have the class members present their findings to the whole class. Note any childhood diseases on the lists such as whooping cough, measles, mumps, and polio that were common at one time but now are seldom seen.

5. **Summarize:** "Communicable diseases are those you can catch, and noncommunicable diseases are those you can't catch. In the next lesson we'll talk about being on the safe side in order to avoid catching communicable diseases."

LESSON 9: PREVENTING COMMUNICABLE DISEASES

Preparation/Materials
- A few grocery items with labels specifying the need to be refrigerated
- Student books
- Unit Evaluation
- Optional: chart paper

Objectives
- Students will identify basic ways to prevent communicable diseases.
- Students will know that the AIDS virus is communicated only through body fluids (blood is specifically mentioned).
- Students will specifically identify refrigeration as a way to be safe with food.

Lesson

1. Ask students to recall the meaning of the terms *communicable* and *noncommunicable.* Tell the class that this lesson will focus on some ways to help us avoid communicable disease.

2. **Student book.** Turn to "What Can You Do to Prevent Communicable Disease?" and read and discuss "One Day..." and "Germs Away" in the student book. Tie in the discussion of bacteria and viruses with previous lesson material on communicable diseases. Mention that some communicable diseases are caused by bacteria and others by viruses (tuberculosis, for example, is caused by bacteria; HIV/AIDS, measles, mumps, chicken pox are caused by viruses).

   Tell students that HIV/AIDS does not spread like other viruses. Most viruses spread to others through food, air, or water. But the HIV/AIDS virus can only live inside the body. It is spread through body fluids such as blood. So one safety rule is to be careful around blood. If a person with HIV/AIDS has a cut or nosebleed, it's important not to touch the blood. If we have a scratch or cut on our hand, the HIV/AIDS virus could get inside of us. Explain how drug users can spread the virus by sharing needles. Sexual contact with someone who has HIV/AIDS is the main way the disease is spread. Stress that HIV/AIDS is very hard for children to get and that most people who get HIV/AIDS are adults.

3. Read "Esther and Irvin Do Their Best," and have students give Esther and Irvin the information they need to keep germs from spreading.

4. Ask students how they can help keep themselves healthy (eating good food, getting enough sleep and exercise, wearing clothing appropriate for the weather, getting health checkups). Stress that our bodies are better able to fight disease when we have good health habits.

5. Read "Why Do You Need Shots?" Talk about the role of shots or immunizations in protecting us from disease (the immune system is studied at higher grade levels). Give students the opportunity to name some kinds of shots they have had. If students have finished their interviews, now is a good time to discuss why their grandparents' childhood illnesses are no longer common in North America.

    Tell students that as yet there is no shot to prevent HIV/AIDS, but scientists all over the world are working very hard to make one.

6. Direct students to read the section "Outsmarting Bacteria" to find out how to keep food from spoiling. During discussion, ask students what the coldest part of the refrigerator is. Explain that bacteria hardly grow at all in the cold. Foods that are going to be kept for a longer period of time should be stored in the freezer. Meat, poultry, and fish, for example, should be stored in the freezer if they will not be used in a few days.

    Ask: "How does your family store leftovers?" Note that most meal leftovers also have to be kept in the refrigerator for safety.

    Have students name foods that can be safely stored on the shelf (crackers, cereals, mixes, flour, sugar, salt, etc.). Answer the "Think It Over"questions.

    1. *To prevent people from getting diseases; to keep diseases from spreading.*
    2. *Washing hands before eating; keeping things out of your mouth; not sharing personal items; washing countertops, etc. in the kitchen. Have students explain why each is important.*
    3. *Poisons made by bacteria.*
    4. *Warm and damp places.*
    5. *Keep dairy products and meat products in the refrigerator.*

7. Show students the sample grocery items. Have volunteers read the labels that specify the need for refrigeration. Note that some foods only need refrigeration after opening.

8. Assign a writing activity. Suggestions:
    *   Have students write sentences telling what they learned in the lesson about avoiding communicable diseases (for example, "I learned to wash fruits and vegetables before I eat them" and "I learned to put some foods in the refrigerator").
    *   Students can write a paragraph about what they can do to get rid of disease germs.

9. **Unit evaluation.** Use the worksheets to review and evaluate. Suggestion: consider asking students to rewrite the false statements of the opening section to make them true.

    True/false: 1 (T), 2 (F), 3 (T), 4 (F), 5 (T), 6 (T), 7 (F), 8 (F), 9 (F), 10 (T)

Short essay:
1. *Answers will vary.*
2. *Height of bike vs. rider's height; working brakes, chain guards, horn, reflectors, condition of tires.*
3. *Answer will vary but would include explaining the danger of electric shock.*
4. *Cancer is a disease that is not carried by a virus or bacteria; it is a disease that can't be "caught."*
5. *Electric shock is a danger because lightning travels through water.*
6. *Answers may include: This must not continue. An adult can make another adult stop or can change the situation so touching doesn't happen again.*

· ·

Related Activities

1. Have students make a list of food shopping tips to make sure food is safe (for example, not buying open packages or dented cans, checking expiration dates on packages, checking for cracked eggs).

2. For a final Safety Snoop log entry for this unit, ask students to observe whether others are being safe as they handle food.

3. Obtain and share with students appropriate resources about HIV/AIDS. Use the resources list or other sources.

4. Study a variety of ways by which foods are kept from spoiling: canning, drying, smoking, salting.

5. Ask a volunteer to research and report on Louis Pasteur and his discovery of a way to make milk safe to drink.

6. Read or place in a center books related to the topic of communicable diseases.

Knowing About Medicines and Drugs

Unit Summary

Lesson 1   Using Medicines
Lesson 2   Know the Facts About Drugs
Lesson 3   Harmful Effects of Smoking
Lesson 4   What's the Message?
Lesson 5   Making Choices About Substances

Goals

- Students will develop awareness of the health hazards of drug abuse.
- Students will choose to be good stewards and avoid drug abuse.

Background

We are all well aware that substance abuse is a serious problem in North American society. *Horizons Health* addresses the problem at each grade level in age-appropriate ways. The curriculum gives students accurate information about health and safety hazards connected with using substances and prepares them to deal with situations that are all too common in our society. It also helps students form correct attitudes toward substances.

In grade 2, students distinguished between prescription and over-the-counter medicines. They also learned about the effects of three drugs that are used frequently in our society—caffeine, nicotine, and alcohol. In grade 3 the discussion of substances is broadened to include methamphetamine. Dose, tolerance, and addiction are other concepts introduced here.

Vocabulary

drug	pharmacist	addiction	prescription medicine
dose	side effects	tolerance	over-the-counter medicine (OTC)
nicotine	cocaine	heroin	marijuana
abuse	substance		

Unit Resources (Search online for similar resources if these are no longer available.)

The Children & Teens section of drugabuse.gov provides a variety of videos and informative sections.

"For Kids & Teens: Tobacco Education Resources."healthychildren.org from the American Academy of Pediatrics.
   A list of tobacco use resources with links, suitable for kids and teens.

"Substance Use." American Academy of Pediatrics, 2020. healthychildren.org.
   Articles written for teens, but this substance use section would be suitable for most ages.

"Videos and Drugs and Addition." Scholastic.
http://headsup.scholastic.com/students/video-collection.
A variety of short videos about drug abuse.

Lesson Resources (Search online for similar resources if these are no longer available)

Lesson 2

About Alcohol and Other Drugs: A Coloring and Activities Book. Channing L. Bete.
Activity book with puzzles, quizzes, and coloring.
Order by visiting https://www.channingbete.com/.
A similar book can be found on https://www.coloringbooksolutions.com/.

"Marijuana: Download the Facts - Printables & Lessons." Scholastic. headsup.scholastic.com.
Four free pdf lessons about marijuana use, suitable for kids.

Lesson 3

"Your Lungs & Respiratory System." KidsHealth from Nemours.
Informative article about lungs and a short video.

"I Don't Think So." Canadian Cancer Society. www.cancer.ca
Activity and coloring book about being tobacco-free.

"Parent Resources: Nicotine Vaping Prevention." CATCH.org.
Free parent resources from the CATCH My Breath Program. The videos and information are
also suitable for kids.

Lesson 5

"Teacher's Guide: Drugs (PreK to Grade 2)." The Nemours Foundation/KidsHealth, 2016.
classroom.kidshealth.org.
Free lesson plan with activities about drug safety.

LESSON 1: USING MEDICINES

Preparation/Materials
- Student books
- Optional: several containers of over-the-counter medicines with clear labels for students to read
- Optional: empty containers of prescription medicines

Objectives
- Students will be aware that medicines are drugs that must be used with proper care.
- Students will understand the proper use of medicinal drugs vs. misuse of medicinal drugs.
- Students will identify ways to feel better without using medicines.

Background
Students will learn that medicines are drugs used for the purpose of fighting disease, preventing disease, or controlling symptoms. Students also will learn about side effects, dosage, and misuse, or abuse, of medicines.

Taking medicine for small aches and pains is a habit that can start when children are quite young. If parents are in this habit, children quickly pick it up. Encourage students to avoid immediately taking medicines for minor ailments and to give other options a try. Often eating nutritious food, resting, doing something active or exercising are the best remedies for restoring body balance.

Lesson

1. Introduce the unit topic. Give students time write down and submit questions they have on the topic of drugs. Tell students that as the unit progresses the class will try to find the answers to the questions.

2. **Student book.** Read and discuss the section "Medicines and Your Body" through the section "Misusing Medicines."

   "Medicines and Your Body." Review three basic uses of medicines and ask students to give examples of medicines in each category. (Antibiotics to help the body fight an ear infection or strep throat, vaccines for preventing measles and mumps, pain blockers for headaches.) Take some time to teach the definition of drugs ("substances other than food that affect how the body works"). Elicit from the class why medicines are also drugs.

   "Prescription Medicines." Review/teach the purpose of prescription medicines. Read the prescription label in the text, and elicit from the class why patient's name, doctor's name, directions for using, date, and the number of refills must all be included. Discuss the importance of taking the right dose. Explain that dose is usually figured by body weight. If you have brought samples of prescription containers, allow students to examine them.

"Over-the-Counter Medicines." Review what over-the-counter medicines are. Have students identify the over-the-counter medicine in the illustration and name some over-the-counter medicines commonly used in their homes. Review that medicines come in different forms—pills, injections, powders, ointments, drops, liquids. Discuss the concept of dose. Explain that the effect of a drug depends on the amount a person takes. Some medicinal drugs are so powerful that even a small amount can be a good-sized dose. "If a little is good, more will be better" does not apply to drugs; a small dose of a medicine may be helpful, but a large dose may be harmful, even dangerous. Stress that this is why it is important to be very careful in use of medicines. If you have brought samples of over-the-counter medicines, give students the opportunity to read the directions for use and the dose on the label.

"Side Effects." Have students define side effects. Ask: "What should a person do who has a side effect from taking a medicine?" (Prescription medicine—notify doctor who prescribed it; over-the-counter—quit taking the medicine; if side effect is serious, consult a doctor.)

"Misusing Medicines." The idea of misusing medicines may be new to students. We are constantly bombarded with ads that promote using medicine for every ache and pain. It's important for students to realize that the body has resources for righting body balance. (For example, the brain produces a pain blocker. However, when people take over-the-counter pain medications, they may suffer rebound headaches when the medication wears off. Their brain has stopped producing its own pain blocker because of the medication.) Suggest that sometimes an upset stomach can be caused by upset feelings or stress. Ask: "How can you help your body then?" (By relaxing. Students will pursue this topic more in the activity that follows.)

Ask students to suggest other ways medicines could be misused (being careless with medicines and not following directions for use/dose; taking medicines prescribed for someone else).

Discuss the "Think It Over" questions.

1. *They can help us get better, they can prevent some illnesses, and they can stop or lessen pain.*
2. *The amount of medicine a person takes at one time.*
3. *Medicine ordered by the doctor for a certain person.*
4. *They have studied the body and know the different kinds and uses of drugs.*
5. *Medicines available without a prescription.*

3. **Student activity.** Divide the class into small groups. Select a reporter and a secretary for each group. Assign each group to make a list of 5–7 suggestions for using medicine safely. The secretaries should write down the suggestions. Give students about 10 minutes for this activity. Then have the reporters read to the class at least two of the items on their lists.

Sort through the items on the lists, deleting duplications and rephrasing rules as necessary. Ask volunteers to copy the rules onto a sheet of paper; duplicate the list for class members.

Consider saving the written work completed during this unit to create books about medicines and drugs. This list of rules can become page 1 of the booklet.

Rules for using medicine safely (Adapted from *Drugs—Your Friends* by Jean B. Leifheit [Standard, 1973]).

- Take medicines only from an adult caregiver.
- Store medicines in a high cabinet out of reach of small children.
- Make sure all medicines are properly labeled and have directions for use.
- Keep medicine containers closed.
- Households with small children should use medicines with safety caps.
- Don't take someone else's prescription medicine.
- If there is a "warning" or "caution" on the medicine label, be sure to follow it.
- Never take more medicine than the directions say—even if the medicine tastes good.
- Never take medicine in the dark.
- Don't play "house" or other games with real medicines.
- If you have only small aches or pains, try to use rest or exercise to help your body solve the problem.
- Don't put medicine in a container labeled as something else.
- Throw away old medicines in a safe way.
- If you have any side effects after taking a medicine, tell an adult about it.

Alternative/additional option: Have student groups think of ways to help feel better without taking medicine (getting rest, eating good food, exercising to relieve stress). What are some enjoyable and relaxing activities? Consider having each member of the group pick one of the ideas to illustrate. Keep their work for unit books.

4. **Closure.** "Medicines are drugs, because they make changes in the body. Medicines, however, are drugs used restore or maintain health. As wonderful as medicines are, we must remember that because they make changes in the body, they must be used with care. Also remember that healthy bodies don't need medicines. We can help our bodies work the best they can by taking care of them."

• •

Related Activities

1. Invite someone from the local poison-control center to talk to the class about the safe use of medicines.

2. Have students make posters showing how to use/store medicine safely. Display the posters in the classroom or school hallway.

LESSON 2: KNOW THE FACTS ABOUT DRUGS

Preparation/Materials
- Art materials for unit booklet covers, class supply
- Student books
- Student Activity
- Optional: pictures of drugs

Objectives
- Students will identify types of nonmedicinal drugs.
- Students will recognize the specific harmful effects that drugs have on the body.

Background

Medicines are drugs that are used to restore or maintain health. Over-the-counter medicines, which are sold under the watchful eye of government agencies, are drugs considered to be safe enough for people to use without a doctor's guidance. Prescription medicines, however, are drugs that have the potential to be harmful, and that's why doctors control their use.

Other drugs have quite a different purpose. These are the mood-altering drugs. Mood–altering drugs can be divided into five major groups: stimulants, depressants, narcotics, hallucinogens, and marijuana/hashish.

Caffeine is a stimulant found in coffee, tea, cola, chocolate, and cocoa. It's also used in some over-the-counter medicines such as diet pills and painkillers. Caffeine speeds up the circulatory and respiratory systems and makes the person feel less tired. Consuming too much caffeine can upset the body balance and make a person nervous, irritable, or wakeful. Although caffeine use may be inadvisable for certain individuals (for example, pregnant women, people with high blood pressure), at this time no studies have proven the negative effects of long-term use.

Nicotine, the colorless chemical found in tobacco, is also a stimulant. It zips from the lungs to the blood stream to the brain, where it acts to stimulate the heart and nervous system. When the body is used to having a certain amount of nicotine in the bloodstream, the person becomes addicted to the drug. (Note: Effects of smoking are covered in more detail in Lesson 3.)

Alcohol is a depressant. It slows down the activity of some areas of the brain, which in turn causes muscles to relax and breathing and heartbeat rates to slow down. Scientists don't really know why, but low doses of alcohol (and other depressants such as barbiturates) make some people feel stimulated.

Cocaine, which produces extreme euphoria, is either sniffed, injected, or smoked. Cocaine is a stimulant and particularly affects the circulatory system and the nervous system. It causes blood vessels to tighten, restricting the flow of oxygen to the brain and nervous system. Some forms of cocaine are very expensive, and for this reason cocaine usually contains large amounts of filler substances. "Crack" is a solidified form of cocaine that is smoked, rather than sniffed or injected. Crack's "high" is more intense and more addictive than that of other forms of cocaine. Because crack is relatively inexpensive, it has contributed to dramatically increased drug use.

Heroin is a narcotic derived from the Asian poppy and is extremely addictive and powerful. Narcotics produce an initial "rushing" sensation, but later they induce a relaxed state. Users are unable to think clearly; they may become drowsy or perhaps restless. Usually their heartbeat slows and breathing is shallow. One of the chief dangers of heroin is overdosing. The effect of an injection lasts for three to six hours, so users must repeat injections periodically to keep the effect constant.

Methamphetamine is a powerful, highly addictive stimulant that affects the central nervous system. Crystal methamphetamine is a form of the drug that looks like glass fragments or shiny, bluish-white rocks. It is chemically similar to amphetamine, a drug used to treat attention-deficit hyperactivity disorder (ADHD) and narcolepsy, a sleep disorder. Methamphetamine increases the amount of the natural chemical dopamine in the brain. Dopamine is involved in body movement, motivation, and reinforcement of rewarding behaviors. The drug's ability to rapidly release high levels of dopamine in reward areas of the brain strongly reinforces drug-taking behavior, making the user want to repeat the experience. Long-term methamphetamine use has many negative consequences, including: extreme weight loss, sleeping problems, violent behavior, paranoia, and severe dental problems.

Marijuana (also called pot, grass, joint, weed, reefer) is partly a depressant and partly a stimulant (its effect depends on the dose and the individual). Marijuana is from the leaves of a common plant *(Cannabis sativa).* The leaves are dried and then cut up and smoked like tobacco. (Hashish is from the flowering tops of the same plant.) Marijuana increases the heart rate and lowers body temperature and blood sugar; it also slows down thinking and affects concentration. Marijuana is not addictive for everyone. (Adapted from *Substance Abuse,* Annette Spence [Friedman, 1989].) Medical marijuana has been made legal in many states and some have made it legal for recreational use.

• •

Lesson

1. Briefly review the previous lesson. What questions submitted by students were answered in the previous lesson? Perhaps read a few questions that will be answered in the course of this lesson.

2. **Student book.** Read and discuss "Know the Facts About Drugs." Make a clear distinction between drugs such as caffeine, nicotine, and alcohol and illegal substances such as heroin, methamphetamine, and cocaine. Discuss the effects of mood-altering drugs, including background information as appropriate.

   Read the section "What Is Tolerance?" Note that when tolerance to drugs such as cocaine develops, people can destroy themselves by overdosing. However, students should also understand that tolerance to medications poses a health problem, too.

   Read "What Is Addiction?" Explain the effects of addiction. Note that many people find it hard to quit smoking because they are addicted to the nicotine. When the body is used to a certain level of nicotine in the bloodstream, it "demands" nicotine.

   The section of the student book "Deciding Not to Spoil Your Body" stresses the responsibility we have to care for our bodies. (The idea of stewardship is developed in more detail in the last lesson of this unit.) Discuss the "Think It Over" questions.

   1. *Caffeine and alcohol.*
   2. *Nicotine.*
   3. *methamphetamine, heroin, cocaine, etc.*
   4. *He or she needs more and more of the drug.*

5. *They become dependent on the drug. Note: dependence can by psychological or physical.*
6. *Answers will vary. Misuse of substances can spoil the body God gave us. We are responsible to God for what we do with our bodies.*

3. **Student activity.** Have students work individually or in groups to complete the word-search activity. (Make sure there is at least one good reader per group.) Students can check with their group members to make sure they have found all the words. If the class is making unit books, collect the activity sheets.

4. Give students time to make covers for their books. Brainstorm several ideas—for example anti-drug slogans ("Just Say No!")—and write them on the board. Direct class members to use one of the slogans on the board or an original slogan as a cover design. Encourage them to create simple, eye-catching designs. Make construction paper and art materials available for the activity.

Display the art work/slogans on the bulletin board until the end of the unit.

5. **Closure.** Ask volunteers to give one fact they've learned about drugs.

Related Activity

• Use resources to reinforce or extend the lesson.
  Suggested options are on the resources list.

LESSON 3: HARMFUL EFFECTS OF SMOKING

Preparation/Materials
- Student Visual
- Student Activity
- Optional: Use a whiteboard or make a transparency of Part 1 of the activity sheet.
- Optional: whiteboard or overhead projector

Objectives
- Students will identify how smoking affects body systems.
- Students will choose not to start smoking.

Background
Tobacco smoke contains about 3,000 chemical compounds. The three major ones are nicotine, tar, and carbon monoxide. Nicotine (see background of previous lesson) is the chemical that causes addiction. It's an oily and colorless chemical. Tar, produced by burning tobacco, is the brown substance that discolors smokers' fingers and teeth. When a smoker inhales, tar enters and sticks to the lungs. Tar is harmful not only because it contains carcinogens but also because it damages the cilia (small hairs that keep out unwanted particles) and the lungs' mucus. Carbon monoxide, a gas that enters the bloodstream during smoking, cuts down on the amount of oxygen the blood carries to parts of the body, which in turn leads to shortness of breath and reduced endurance during physical activity.

Someone who smokes heavily and over a long period of time runs the risk of contracting chronic bronchitis, emphysema, heart disease, and lung and other cancers.

A distinction is made between mainstream smoke, smoke that a smoker inhales, and sidestream smoke, smoke emitted from the burning end of the tobacco. Sidestream smoke has been found to increase the risk of lung disease (especially in children) and asthma attacks and to cause irritation of eyes, nose, and throat, as well as allergic reactions.

In recent years smokeless tobacco in the form of chewing tobacco or snuff has become increasingly popular. Baseball players are the most visible users of chewing tobacco. Chewing tobacco, which has sweeteners and flavoring mixed in with coarsely ground tobacco leaves, can lead to gum disease, tooth loss, heart disease, and cancer of the mouth, throat, and esophagus.

Lesson
1. Ask: "How can we honor God with our bodies?" (Answers will vary, but encourage answers that stress the positive: taking care of our bodies, living a healthy life.) What does honoring God with our bodies have to do with medicines, drugs, and smoking?" (As God's children, we don't want to abuse God's gift of life or any other gifts he has given us.)

Be sensitive during the discussion to children whose parents smoke. Try to steer the class away from judgmental attitudes. Recall the problem of addiction—once people get "hooked" on nicotine and their bodies demand the substance, it's very hard to quit. Consider drawing a comparison to an activity students may find very hard to control such as playing video games or watching TV.

2. Refer to the visual in the student workbook. Use the following information to describe how smoking affects body parts and systems.
   - The mouth helps you draw smoke into your windpipe and lungs. Consequently, the mouth and throat tissues may feel irritated.
   - The lungs deliver smoke to the bloodstream, which carries it to all parts of the body. At the same time, some of these smoke particles settle in the lung's tiny tubes.
   - The brain stimulates hormones that make you feel slightly stimulated or relaxed.
   - The heart rate increases.
   - Blood vessels constrict and the blood pressure rises.
   - The stomach is affected as hunger is depressed.
   - The adrenal glands make other mood-altering hormones.
   - Urine is inhibited when the kidneys come into contact with smoke substances. (*Encyclopedia of Good Health: Substance Abuse* by Annette Spence, p. 22)

   During the presentation you may also wish to include facts from the lesson background.

3. **Student activity.** Refer students to the activity in their student workbooks. Consider making Part 1 a whole class activity. Using a whiteboard or the overhead projector and a transparency of Part 1, work with the class to fill in the chart. Elicit from the class the advantages and disadvantages of smoking, of living with a smoker, and of chewing tobacco. As you write the responses in the appropriate sections on the transparency, students should also be recording the responses on the worksheet. (Another option: have student groups work together to list advantages and disadvantages in each category on the worksheet.)

   Assign students to complete Part 2 of the activity and write about what they plan to decide about smoking. As you discuss this section, you may wish to note that it's better not to start smoking because once a person is addicted to nicotine, it's very difficult to quit.

4. Have students create T-shirt designs using no smoking slogans. Sample: "You'll Win If You Don't Begin." Display the T-shirt designs in the classroom—at least until the class members are assembling their books.

LESSON 4: WHAT'S THE MESSAGE?

Preparation/Materials
- Samples of advertisements for cigarettes, OTCs, and alcohol. If possible, enlarge the ads for easier viewing.
- For student activity:
  magazines with lots of ads, class supply scissors and glue or tape
- Student Activity

Objectives
- Students will be able to identify the hidden messages of advertisements for tobacco products and OTCs (include alcohol if you wish).
- Students will develop ability to critically evaluate ads.

Background
Companies spend billions of dollars on advertising in order to convince us to buy their products. Most advertisements are carefully and cleverly created to make us believe that using the product will bring us fun, happiness, friends, beauty, sex appeal, wealth, or good health.

Tobacco advertising, for example, may show groups of attractive people smoking and having a marvelous time. The implicit message is that smoking will bring us similar pleasures. The reality is that smoking can cause serious health problems for smokers and nonsmokers and that the smell that is emitted from a smoker's lungs and clothing may bring unpleasant reactions from others.

Some changes in tobacco advertising have taken place in North America in the last decade. Warnings about its harmful effects are required on tobacco products, and no cigarette ads are allowed on TV. Tobacco advertising is also banned from Olympic sports facilities. Tobacco companies no longer picture star athletes in cigarette ads. However, many sports arenas do carry giant billboards advertising cigarettes, giving companies a simple way to picture their cigarette brands with star athletes.

OTC advertisers often show a before-using-the-product and an after-using-the-product picture: the person in obvious discomfort, alone or isolated from the fun-loving crowd, and the same person in good health, happy and enjoying life. The message? The OTC drug will solve the problem simply and totally. It also gives the more subtle message that drugs make it unnecessary to experience pain, embarrassment, or isolation. This misleading message makes abuse of other substances more likely. Besides, in reality, the misuse of OTCs (and prescription) drugs can cause serious physical and psychological damage. And the warnings about possible harmful effects of OTCs are often understated or appear in very small print.

• •

Lesson
1. Begin by talking about advertising aimed at children that usually accompanies (and pays for) cartoons and other children's programs. Elicit from students how the advertising affects them. Do they ever ask or nag parents to buy specific toys, cereals, or other things they see advertised? Why do they want what's been advertised? If students have obtained the advertised products, ask whether the product lived up to the advertisement.

2. Display the sample ads. Read and discuss each one, leading students to understand how advertisements persuade us to buy a product. Use questions such as the following during the discussion:
   - What product is the ad selling?
   - What messages does the ad send?
   - Does the product appear to be something good? Why?
   - Will this product really do what the ad suggests?
   - Are there negative effects connected with using the product that the ad is covering up or not telling you about?

3. **Student activity.** Students, working in groups, should look through magazines to find at least five OTC, tobacco, or alcohol ads that send one or more of the messages discussed.

   Next, have students complete the activity in the student workbook. Have each student choose one of the ads, analyze it, and answer the questions on the worksheet. Students can glue or tape their ads to the bottom of the page or to the back of the page. These worksheets can also become part of the unit books.

4. **Closure.** Give students opportunity to share their ads and insights. How will what students have learned about advertising make a difference?

• •

Related Activity

- Have students create negative ads for OTCs, cigarettes, alcohol, or "street drugs" such as cocaine or heroin. The ads should reflect the harmful results of substance abuse.

LESSON 5: MAKING CHOICES ABOUT SUBSTANCES

Preparation/Materials
- Student Activity
- Materials needed for assembling books
- Unit Evaluation

Objectives
- Students will consider the relationship between being God's stewards and the use/abuse of substances.
- Students will review unit concepts.
- Students will choose to avoid substance abuse.

Lesson

1. Talk with the class about what it means to be God's stewards. Read Bible passages that speak of our responsibility as stewards over money (for example, Luke 19:11–26) and over our bodies (1 Corinthians 6:19–20).

2. Lead a brief review. Draw a contrast between the use of medicinal drugs to help maintain or restore health and the abuse of drugs. Tie in with the discussion of stewardship in Step 1. Stress that it's up to each person to make wise decisions about drugs.

3. **Student activity.** Students should complete the activity sheet by writing what they would think or say in each situation. When students complete their work, discuss the responses. As you talk about the situation, spend some time thinking of ways students can say no to the offer of a cigarette (or other drug) firmly, but without being abusive or insulting.

4. Have students assemble their books, using as covers the artwork incorporating anti-drug slogans. Books include the following pages:
   - Word Search
   - List of rules for safe use of medicines
   - "What's the Score?" (including T-shirt design) activity sheet
   - "What's the Message?" activity sheet
   - "It's up to You" activity sheet

5. **Unit evaluation.** Use the worksheets to review and evaluate. You may wish to have students rewrite the false statements in the first section to make them true.

   True/false: 1 (T), 2 (T), 3 (F), 4 (F), 5 (F), 6 (T), 7 (T), 8 (T)
   Short essay:
   1. *Answers will vary.*
   2. *Hard to quit, bad for health, ugly teeth and bad breath, waste of money, not taking proper care of God's great gift—our bodies.*

3. *Answers will vary.*
4. *Lie down awhile, rest, eat some food, get some exercise.*
5. *Prescription medicines are strong medicines; only a doctor should decide if you should have it. The amount or dose varies according to weight, age, etc.*

●●●

Related Activities

1. Extend the lesson by using materials from the resouces list or by showing informational video clips.

2. Have students, using their books as a reference, work together to make a big book for presentation on using medicines safely for younger students.

Building a Healthy Lifestyle

Goals

- Students will recognize the basic elements of a healthy lifestyle: proper nutrition, dental care, sufficient sleep, and fitness.
- Students will be introduced to various health agencies and their roles in the community.

Background

This unit deals with basic, personal health-care issues—nutrition, dental care, getting enough rest, and fitness. It also raises awareness about health-care products and health resources available in the community. The stress is on helping students become aware of the health choices they make each day, so that from a young age they begin to assume responsibility for taking care of their bodies and form healthy patterns of living. But beyond developing basic living skills and healthy habits, students need to understand why taking care of their bodies is important.

North American society sends confusing signals to children about the value of a person's body. On the one hand, there is the body cult, which makes an idol of the body. Shaping, strengthening, clothing, decorating, and gratifying the body is the central focus of some people's lives. This is a form of self-glorification and self-idolatry. On the other hand, our society has large numbers of persons who treat their bodies carelessly, ignoring basic nutrition and physical exercise or living at a too-strenuous pace. Carried to an extreme, this view leads to self-destruction. These contrasting views, however, share an underlying attitude that says, "This is my body. And what I do with my body is my business."

Christians believe that because "we are not our own," how we treat our bodies is not an individual matter. The kingly rule of Christ extends over the body, too. The body must not become an idol, but it should be treated with respect. After all, God created the human body and breathed life into it. In fact, God charged humans to be caretakers of creation (Genesis 1:28). As God's people we are called to care for the body and use it in the service of God and others.

Vocabulary

cells	posture	gum	roots	permanent teeth
nutrients	protein	acid	endurance	primary teeth
nutritionists	calcium	plaque	responsibility	tooth parts:
consumer	flexibility	carbohydrates		enamel
fluoride	endurance	physical fitness		crown

Unit Resources (Search online for similar resources if these are no longer available.)

"MyPlate Kids' Place." ChooseMyPlate U.S. Department of Agriculture.
https://www.choosemyplate.gov/browse-by-audience/view-all-audiences/children/kids.
The website contains printable worksheets and activities sorted by age group.

"Healthy Eating Toolkit." Action for Healthy Kids.
https://www.actionforhealthykids.org/nutrition-toolkit/
This page contains blog posts, ideas, and activities for kids.

"Physical Activity Facts." Centers for Disease Control and Prevention.
Information and downloadable pdfs focused around youth.

"Exercise Tips for Kids and Teens." NASM.
Resource containing information about benefits, exercise frequency, movements, and risks.

"Get Moving Activities for Grades 3-5." Wide Open School.
A variety of videos and activities to get kids physically active.

Lesson Resources (Search online for similar resources if these are no longer available.)

Lessons 2–3
Resources section of the MyPlate website. Contains many overview videos and videos suitable for kids.

Food Hero. Oregon State University. https://foodhero.org/kids.
Kid-friendly recipes that are paired with information sheets about nutrition. Printables and videos are also available.

"7 Nutrition Activities for Elementary and Middle School Students." Houghton Mifflin Harcourt.
List of activities that includes links.

"Stay Home. Stay Fit." Fit kids. https://fitkids.org/homeworkouts/.
Easy to follow routines and videos for kids.

"Physical Activity Facts." Centers for Disease Control and Prevention.
Information and downloadable pdfs focused around youth.

Lessons 4–5
The American Dental Association provides a variety of information and resources for different ages groups through www.mouthhealthy.org.

Smile Smarts Dental Health Curriculum. Mouth Healthy, American Dental Association.
https://www.mouthhealthy.org/en/resources/lesson-plans/smile-smarts.
Printable PDFs separated by different grade levels.

Toothbrushing with Charlie Brown. Videocassette. Chicago: American Dental Association.
This five-minute video is one of several videos on tooth care available from the American
Dental Association. This video can be foundonline.

Lesson 6
Showers, Paul. Sleep is for Everyone. Let's-Read-and-Find-Out Science Book. New York: Crowell,
1974.
Available through Barnes and Noble.

"Why Do I Need to Sleep?" KidsHealth from Nemours. www.kidshealth.org.
Related topics are linked to this short webpage, written for kids.

Lesson 7
"Get Moving Activities for Grades 3-5." Wide Open School.
A variety of videos and activities to get kids physically active.

"Healthy Family Home." YMCA. https://www.ymca.net/healthy-family-home.
Web page provides links to different topics that contain pdfs and ideas for families.

Lesson 8
"Poor Posture: Fixing It Before It Becomes a Problem." Nationwide Children's Hospital.
www.nationwidechildrens.org.

Lesson 10
A short video for kids and a sample activity is available at apwa.net as part of their Discovering
the World of Public Words program (K-5). Consider also looking at your county website for local
information about public works.

Lesson 11
"Healthy Living." Brittanica Kids. kids.brittanica.com.
This short webpage for kids also has links about specific health-related topics.

LESSON 1: CELLS—THE SMALLEST BUILDING BLOCKS

Preparation/Materials
- Picture of an Eqyptian pyramid
- Student books
- Clay or plasticine, enough for one small lump per student
- Optional: microscope(s) and prepared slides of various types of cells

Objectives
- Students will be introduced to the concept of cells.
- Students will recognize the importance of nutrition in the building of their bodies.

Background
The human body is made up of various types of cells. Each type has a special job. There are skin cells, bone cells, blood cells, brain cells, muscles cells, and many other types. Cells are so tiny that they can only be seen through a microscope. Cells multiply by dividing—and that's how a human being grows from a single cell to a complete human being.

Oxygen and food substances enter the cell through its outer skin or membrane, and carbon dioxide and waste products are let out through the same membrane. The bloodstream is the body's delivery system. It serves the cells, transporting digested food substances, which enter the bloodstream from the intestine, and oxygen, which enters from the lungs. It also cleans the cells and carries waste products on their way out of the body.

This lesson on the cell precedes the discussion of nutrition in order to give students a clear idea of the importance of nutrition. Where does the food we eat go? Why does it matter what we eat? Stress that God has given us marvelously designed bodies, and to help our bodies grow and stay healthy, we must build a healthy lifestyle.

Lesson
1. If you have access to microscopes, introduce the lesson by inviting the children to look at the prepared slides of various types of cells with the use of the microscopes. Don't tell them what they are viewing. When everyone has had an opportunity to view the slides, ask class members to describe what they saw. Because cells from different human tissues look different, you will receive a variety of answers. Tell the students that what they have seen are called cells and that these cells were taken from various parts of the body. Cells of the same kind are grouped together to do a certain job in the body.

2. Show students a picture of an Egyptian pyramid, or ask students to describe a pyramid. Elicit from them that even though pyramids are huge, each one began with a single chunk of stone and was built by placing one stone on top of the other. Make a comparison to body structure. Millions of cells make up each part of the body.

3. **Student book.** Have students turn to the section "Your Smallest Building Block—the Cell" and read "What Is Your Body Made Of?" and "How Do You Grow?" Identify what important things we need in order to live and grow (food, water, oxygen). Answer the "Think It Over" questions.

    1. *Some cells divide and make new cells.*
    2. *Answers will vary. Stress basics of a healthy lifestyle: eating healthy food, exercising, and getting sufficient rest.*

4. Have students divide a piece of clay to demonstrate the principle of cell division. Give each student a small lump of clay or plasticine. Explain that each human begins as *one* cell. Direct the class to divide the clay in half and then to keep on dividing each piece until there are at least 16 "cells."

5. Ask students to identify the basics that cells need in order to live and grow: food, water, oxygen. How do what we eat and drink and what we breathe get to our cells? Have the class answer the question by reviewing the diagrams of the respiratory, circulatory, and digestive body systems in the student book.

6. Close the lesson by telling students that this unit is going to be about building a healthy lifestyle. Elicit from them or explain what a lifestyle is. You may wish to recall or refer to the introduction of the student book, which explains why healthy living is important and how daily choices affect health.

LESSON 2: EATING FOR GOOD HEALTH

Preparation/Materials
- Student books
- For bingo game:
  Student Activities 1 and 2
  die or spinner labeled with five food groups
  bingo chips or construction paper circles,
      class supply
- Optional: large picture of a combination food (for example, a sandwich or slice of pizza)

Objectives
- Students will learn/review basic food groups.
- Students will recognize how combination foods fit into food groups.
- Students will recognize the function and sources of nutrients.

Background
What is nutrition? According to *Food and Your Child* (Successful Parenting Series, TimeLife, 1988), nutrition is the way the body takes in and uses food. Food is broken down by our digestive system into nutrients—chemical substances that promote growth, build and maintain cells, and help regulate body processes. Nutritionists have divided foods into groups according to the major nutrients they supply. Food from the grain group provides carbohydrates, a nutrient that provides energy.

Food from the fruit and vegetable groups supply many vitamins. The nutrient vitamin A has many functions, but its role in night vision is one of the best known; the nutrient vitamin C is equally important, and one of its functions is to combine with protein to form collagen, a sticky substance that binds cells and connective tissue together to help repair wounds. The dairy group provides the nutrient calcium, which is necessary to build strong bones and teeth. The meat group supplies protein the body needs for growth and strong muscles.

Nutritionists have established guidelines for the amounts and types of food people should eat. MyPlate organizes foods into the following five groups: grains group (5 ounces); fruits group (2 cups); vegetables group (2 cups); dairy group (2 cups); and the protein group (5 ounces). MyPlate graphically illustrates the relative importance of the groups. An illustration of MyPlate can be found in the student booklet.

As students classify foods in this lesson, they will be dealing with combination foods. Children eat many combination foods, and it's helpful for them to begin to consider the nutritional value of these foods. A combination food includes ingredients from two or more of the five food groups. Combination foods are as nutritious as their component parts.

Lesson
1. **Student book.** Have students turn to the section "Nutrition and You." Enjoy Arnold Adoff's poem "Not Me But" and talk about the poet's love of food—and students' love of food.

   Read and discuss "What Are Nutrients?"

Study MyPlate and lead students to discover what the construction of MyPlate shows about relative values of the different food groups. If students are already familiar with the five food groups, explain why nutritionists are restructuring food groups (refer to lesson background). As you identify each group, review/elicit from students how each group contributes to health (grain group provides carbohydrates to give us energy; vegetables and fruits groups provide important vitamins; protein group supplies protein necessary for building and repairing body cells; dairy group provides the nutrient calcium that helps build strong bones and teeth). Fats, oils, and sweets are not included on MyPlate since they are to be used sparingly. Review the process of producing foods from grains to ensure that students understand why bread, pasta, cereals, etc., belong in this group (wheat—flour—bread).

Explain that the daily requirements mentioned are the daily minimum. Children should eat that minimum amount (children's servings will be smaller than adult servings). Stress that eating a wide variety of foods is the best way to get proper nutrients. Use the "Think It Over" questions as you discuss the material.

1. *To thank God for the food and ask God's blessing on it. Discuss how this prayer shows that we recognize God as the giver of food and life.*
2. *The part of food/substance in food the body needs for health and growth.*
3. *The study of food and its relationship to health.*
4. *To be sure that we ingest a variety of nutrients.*
5. *Answers will vary.*
6. *They should be used sparingly.*

2. **Student activity.** Play the Food Group Bingo game. Have students complete the activity page in the student workbook. Have students create individual bingo cards by cutting apart the pictures and then gluing 24 of them onto the second page (remind students to leave the "FREE" space open). Students may glue the pictures in any order they wish.

Before you begin playing the game, take time to identify the pictures of combination foods and decide the food groups they contain. Lead students to identify, for example, that cheese pizza is made up of grain plus cheese plus tomato sauce. Do the same thing for other combination foods represented. Make it clear that combination foods are as nutritious as their ingredients.

Distribute bingo chips to each student. Use the spinner or throw the die (label the die with food group names or perhaps establish that a number 1 will be grain, etc.). As you call out the name of a food group, students choose one food of that group to cover. Play for a straight row, a diagonal row, or other chosen variation. When a student gets bingo, have him or her call out the name of the foods and which group they belong to. Play several times to give students practice in classifying foods.

This game is adapted from *Food Keeps Me Healthy*, produced by the National Dairy Council (1987).

Related Activities

1. Focus on combination foods. Brainstorm a list of combination foods, break down the different ingredients, and make a food chain for each. Have students dream up combination foods that include several foods they like. Have them name and draw pictures of their creations. Consider having them develop commercials for their "new" foods.

2. Have volunteers help you to make a large poster of MyPlate, using the picture in the student book as a model. Students could cut each food group section from a different color construction paper, mount MyPlate on tagboard, and then glue magazine pictures of representative foods in each section. Or you could use markers to draw the outline of MyPlate on tagboard and then have students place magazine pictures of representative foods in the correct space on the plate.

3. Integrate with language arts. Students can write and illustrate their own poems expressing their feelings about food or write directions for making a favorite sandwich or breakfast. Or have them create stories that use as many food expressions as possible (examples: being in a jam or full of beans/baloney, being nuts about someone, calling someone cupcake or honey).

4. Enjoy reading other poems or stories about food. Suggested poems: "My Mouth" and "Chocolate Chocolate" by Arnold Adoff, "Egg Thoughts" by Russell Hoban, and "Taste of Purple" by Leland B. Jacobs in *The Random House Book of Poetry for Children*.

5. Invite parents or others of varying ethnic heritage to talk about ethnic foods. If possible, sample various ethnic foods.

LESSON 3: SMART SNACKS

Preparation/Materials

- Student Activities 1 and 2
- Optional: Have each student contribute one item for a class smart-snack party.

Objectives

- Students will recognize the function and role of snacking in relation to their eating habits.
- Students will identify healthy snacks.

Background

Sensible snacking makes nutritional sense for children. Normally active children have high energy needs. Besides, because children have small stomachs, eating in small installments suits their needs. By spacing food throughout the day, children can receive a regular supply of energy and nutrients.

The key to good snacking is choosing snacks from the basic food groups. Such snacks should contribute nutrients and not just empty calories. Another important consideration is avoiding sticky sugary snacks that can cause tooth decay. Whenever we eat these types of foods, bacteria in the mouth produces acid for about 20 minutes, and these acid attacks increase the risk of cavities. How much sugar we eat, how often we eat it, how long the sugar stays in the mouth (suckers and gum stay a long time), and the stickiness of the food are all factors that contribute to the formation of cavities. Be aware, however, that eating foods high in sugar is less harmful to teeth if those foods are eaten with meals because the acid is neutralized by saliva produced during a meal.

In teaching this lesson, identify (1) snacks that are nutritious and low in sugar and can be eaten anytime in moderation; (2) snacks that are high in fat, salt, or sugar and therefore should only be eaten occasionally; and (3) snacks that are very sticky and high in sugar and should be avoided.

- -

Lesson

1. **Student activity.** Assign students to record all the food they eat in a 24-hour period using the record sheet in Student Activity 1. If possible, students should complete this before the class session begins.

   Review the students' record sheets and ask them to classify the foods according to food groups. Students will need help with this. Consider having them do this exercise in groups so that they can help each other.

   Help students evaluate their day's intake with questions such as the following:
   - "How many foods did you eat from each group?" Have students compare their totals with the amounts suggested on the MyPlate guide.
   - "Did you eat at regular times during the day?"
   - "Did you eat a nutritious breakfast?"
   - "Did you eat a variety of foods?"
   - "Were your snacks mainly nutritious snacks?"

Consider giving students time to circle trouble areas on their chart or to write on the back of their activity sheet the food group(s) they need to eat more of.

2. Talk specifically about snacks. Let children name some snacks they ate that were nutritious. Ask students for their ideas on what makes a healthy snack. After they provide several suggestions, discuss what these suggestions have in common (ingredients are from basic food groups and are nutritious; low in sugar). Note that snacks that are high in fat, salt, or sugar should only be eaten occasionally. Also elicit from students why sugary, sticky snacks lead to tooth decay. Review the chain of tooth decay:

   sugar + bacteria = acid
   acid + tooth enamel = tooth decay or cavities

3. **Student activity.** Challenge students to use their knowledge of good snacking to think of five smart snacks that would sell in a "snack store." Consider setting prices on items and having students work out some math problems on the bottom or back of the worksheet (Student Activity 2).

   Examples:
   If a customer bought B and E, she or he would spend _____.
   If a customer paid for C with a $5 bill, how much change would he or she receive?

4. Close the lesson by eating a smart snack with the class. Have a simple snack of popcorn or cheese and crackers, or if students brought various items from home, have a tasting party.

• •

Related Activities

1. Create posters to encourage healthy snacking.

2. Ask each student to share a recipe for a favorite nutritious snack and compile a class snack booklet.

3. Make word searches that include names of smart snacks. Student pairs may enjoy working on these. Pairs can exchange puzzles and circle the smart snacks.

4. Show a filmstrip or video on the lesson topic. Nutrition videios can be found on pbskids.org and nutrition.gov.

LESSON 4: LEARNING ABOUT TEETH

Preparation/Materials
- Student books
- Student Activity

Objectives
- Students will develop familiarity with the structure and function of teeth.
- Students will develop an understanding of primary and permanent dentition.

Background
The tooth's outer layer is enamel and provides a strong biting surface. In fact, enamel, which is made of non-living tissue, is the hardest substance in the body. The body of the tooth is made of dentine, a substance quite a bit similar to bone. The center of the tooth is composed of soft tissue called pulp. In the pulp are blood vessels, which supply the tooth with food and oxygen, and nerves, which make the tooth sensitive to temperature and pain. The tooth is anchored in the jawbone by a thin layer of tissue called cementum.

• •

Lesson (1-2 sessions)

1. Introduce the topic of this lesson by asking students to think about the shape and structure of their teeth. Ask students to swish their tongue around their mouth and over each tooth. How do they think their teeth are shaped? Perhaps have students come to the board and draw shapes of teeth. Are the teeth all shaped alike? What accounts for the various shapes? Elicit from students or explain what the various jobs of teeth are: the front teeth (incisors) are for biting and cutting food, cuspids or canines are for tearing and breaking, bicuspids are for grinding and tearing, molars are for mashing and grinding (types of teeth are covered in more detail in grade 4). What functions do teeth have besides preparing food for swallowing? (Speaking—particularly sounds such as *d, t, th, l, v,* and *f.*)

   Next ask volunteers to tell what they know about what a tooth is made of. Accept all responses, telling the class that in this lesson they'll find out more about teeth.

2. **Student book.** Have students open their books to "Taking Care of Your Teeth" and read the section entitled "Parts of a Tooth." Refer to the picture to identify each part of the tooth. When the class has finished reading "Parts of a Tooth," ask students to explain in their own words the job of each of these tooth parts: enamel, roots, blood vessels, and nerves. Ask: "What kind of messages do you think a nerve in a tooth with a cavity would send to the brain? ("Ouch! Do something about that hole right away"; "This food is cold/hot!") Why are these messages important?" (They are warning signals that we need for our protection.)

   Read "Set 1 and Set 2," which deals with the shedding and erupting patterns of teeth. Ask if any students currently have loose teeth or have recently lost a tooth. (Be sure to note that the ages of shedding primary teeth is approximate; students who still have quite a few primary teeth may be sensitive on this point.)

Stress the importance of taking care of primary teeth, explaining that primary teeth function as guides for incoming permanent teeth and if primary teeth are lost too soon, permanent teeth may have inadequate space and not come in as they should. Dentists often place space maintainers if primary teeth are lost too soon. Use the comparison (suggested by the American Dental Association) of losing a stone from the arch of a building. Just as a builder preserves the arch by replacing a stone, a dentist uses a space maintainer or artificial tooth to protect the dental arch. Perhaps make a simple sketch on the board to illustrate the comparison.

3. **Student activity.** Have students review lesson terms by completing the word search and definitions. If time permits, consider asking students to turn over their work sheets and try to draw from memory a diagram of a tooth. Can they label its main parts? Students can check their drawings against the one provided in the student booklet.

1. *cavity*   2. *blood*   3. *nerves*   4. *plaque*   5. *enamel*   6. *crown*

Related Activities

1. Integrate with language arts and assign students to write about what happened and how they felt when they lost their first tooth. If they can't remember, suggest that they create a story about someone losing a tooth. Students can illustrate their stories.

2. Make riddles about parts or functions of a tooth or make flash cards of lesson terms and use them to work with partners to review lesson terms.

3. Find out about types of animal teeth. Students can check their pet's teeth. What kinds of teeth do carnivores, herbivores, and insectivores have? What are omnivores? One resource is *Foodworks* from the Ontario Science Centre.

LESSON 5: TAKING CARE OF YOUR TEETH

Preparation/Materials

- Optional: Invite a resource person such as a dental hygienist to demonstrate proper oral hygiene.
- Optional: model of teeth and toothbrush for demonstrating brushing
- Optional: package of toothpaste containing fluoride
- Toothbrushes and disclosing tablets, class supply. (Often toothbrushes and disclosing tablets are available free of charge from a local or national dental association or neighborhood dentist.)
- Optional: small mirrors for student use
- Student books

Objectives

- Students will review the cause of tooth decay.
- Students will learn ways to prevent tooth decay.
- Students will practice oral hygiene skills.

Background

According to American Dental Association statistics, 3 primary teeth of the average six-year-old child have been attacked by decay at least once. And by age 21, the average adult has 11 decayed, missing, or filled teeth. So neglecting daily personal oral care during youth has severe effects. The chief problem in children's oral health is dental caries—cavities.

A dental cavity is not just a hole in a tooth. Rather it is the result of a bacterial infection. Plaque—"a soft, sticky, colorless layer of bacteria and their byproducts" that is constantly forming—sticks to the teeth. Then when the person eats a food containing sugar, the bacteria break down the food and change the sugar to acid. After repeated acid attacks, the tooth's enamel is penetrated, bacteria enter the tooth, and a cavity results.

Reducing sugar in the diet is one way of reducing cavities. But the amount of sugar is not the only problem. The dental association stresses that "frequency of eating sugar-rich food, the length of time the sugar stays in the mouth, and the physical form of the food (such as sticky sweets) are all important factors in producing cavities."

Another way to reduce cavities is to remove the plaque by brushing and flossing. One of the best ways to educate children about plaque is to use a disclosing solution (a harmless vegetable dye), so that they can actually see the plaque on their teeth.

Valuable resources for these lessons are local dentists, hygienists, or community organizations interested in school health education. They may also be able to provide helpful educational materials and/or a model for demonstrating tooth cleaning techniques.

If dental kits with disclosing agents and toothbrushes are available, you may wish to arrange for the class to use the disclosing agents, brush teeth, and then use the disclosing agent once more. If this is not feasible at school, have students do this at home with parents supervising and then have them report on the experience.

Lesson

1. **Student book.** Review the plaque chain: plaque + sugar = acid; acid + tooth enamel = teeth = tooth decay or cavities. Read the section "Plaque Attack" in the student book and discuss the results of plaque's work demonstrated in the picture of a decaying

tooth. Explain that if plaque is not removed daily, it can cause the gums to become red and sore and to bleed during brushing. Plaque that is not removed becomes hard and forms calculus, which can lead to gum (periodontal) disease.

2. Elicit from students ways to break the plaque chain. Check their suggestions against the list provided in the student book as you read "Tooth Savers." Ask students to give reasons why each tip can help save teeth. Note that during regular dental checkups dentists can spot cavities while they're still small and fix them. And the professional cleaning job of the teeth helps to remove calculus.

Write the word *fluoride* on the board and briefly talk about the role of fluoride in preventing tooth decay: fluoride strengthens enamel, making it resistant to decay. (Is fluoride added to the community water supply? If no one knows, assign volunteers to research the question.) Note that sometimes dentists directly apply fluoride to teeth or recommend use of products containing fluoride. If you have a product containing fluoride, show it to the students.

3. Discuss/demonstrate how to brush teeth. If a resource person has been invited, ask him or her to show the class brushing/flossing techniques and discuss oral hygiene. Otherwise ask the class members how they brush their teeth. Then demonstrate or talk about how to brush and floss. Stress covering all surfaces of the teeth—outside, inside, tops. Point out how to reach the inside of the front teeth, an area that is apt to be missed.

How to remove plaque can be taught more easily if students can see the plaque. If you were able to get toothbrushes and disclosing tablets for each student, distribute the articles. Students should open the packages carefully and brush their teeth in the bathroom. Have each child chew a disclosing tablet after brushing and then examine their teeth and gums (either in the bathroom mirror or with handheld ones). The color left on the teeth shows the plaque still remaining to be removed.

Use the "Think It Over" questions to review this section.

1. *Stress that primary teeth keep a space so the permanent tooth can come in straight.*
2. *Bacteria in plaque combine with sugar in teeth to make an acid that eats away the tooth.*
3. *Brush; floss; avoid sweet, sticky foods; eat healthy foods.*
4. *Answers will vary.*

4. **Closure.** "We need our teeth to eat and to talk and to give shape to our face. Our primary teeth are important for guiding our permanent teeth into place. Our permanent teeth are the set of teeth that have to last a lifetime. How can we take care of our teeth?"

Have students take toothbrushes home. Encourage them to brush their teeth at least every night and preferably twice a day.

Related Activities

1. Provide a toothbrushing chart for one month (two spaces per day for morning and evening brushing/flossing). Encourage children to fill in the chart with a simple yes/no. All completed charts might deserve a sugarless treat!

2. Do an experiment to demonstrate how acid produced by plaque can eat into a tooth. Place pieces of eggshell in two cups. Cover the pieces in one cup with water and the other with vinegar (an acid). Explain that similar to teeth, eggshells are mainly made of calcium. Let the cups with eggshells stand until the liquid in both cups has evaporated. Discuss the results. Or for a more dramatic experiment obtain some extracted teeth from a dentist, let them soak in a 5 percent solution of sulphuric acid (available, often free of charge, from a pharmacy), and watch the teeth begin to immediately dissolve.

3. Write a class thank-you note to the resource person.

4. Use materials suggested in Lesson Resources to extend or reinforce the lesson.

LESSON 6: SLEEP TIGHT

Preparation/Materials
- For clock activity:
  paper plates, one per student
  paper fasteners, one per student
  construction paper and scissors
- Student books

Objectives
- Students will identify sufficient rest as a component of healthy living.
- Students will recognize the effects of too little sleep.

Background
The time we spend asleep is necessary for our brain to relax and recover from the day's mental exercise. Our bodies also need time to replace worn-out cells and provide rest for muscles. Sufficient sleep lets all the important parts of our body rest so we can wake with renewed energy, ready to enjoy the day and to serve God.

• •

Lesson

1. Begin the lesson by focusing on the effects of being tired. Ask students to complete (orally or in writing) several sentences such as the following:
   - Being tired makes me feel...
   - I can tell when my brother/sister/teacher/pet is tired because...
   - Once when I was tired, I...
   - I don't like being around people who are tired because...
   - Being rested makes me feel...

2. **Student book.** Ask: "Why do we need sleep?" Discuss the students' suggestions and then read "Sleep for Health" in the student book. Stress that people need varying amounts of sleep and that sometimes we may need extra sleep when we exert ourselves physically or are not feeling well. Discuss the "Think It Over" questions.

   1. *Stress that we need sleep so that our bodies can rest, grow, and repair themselves.*
   2. *Answers will vary.*
   3. *Answers will vary. Note that operating machines is very unsafe when we're very tired.*
   4. *Answers will vary. In discussion bring in the need of sufficient sleep in order to do our best and serve God.*

3. **Student activity.** Give each student a paper plate, paper fastener, and two construction-paper strips for clock hands. Direct students to make a clock by printing numbers carefully on the plate (starting with 12, 3, 6, and 9 and then filling in the others). Have students attach the hands with the paper fasteners and show the time they usually go to bed. (Review appropriate place of hour hand if minute hand is pointing past the half hour.)

Then instruct students to show what time they wake up. Ask them to calculate the number of hours they usually sleep each night. Is it enough? Do they feel energetic and ready to face the day when they awake in the morning? Close the lesson by summarizing or eliciting from students why its important to get enough sleep.

• •

Related Activities

1. Create posters focusing on one reason for getting enough sleep.

2. Use student resources on the topic of sleep to reinforce or extend the lesson.

LESSON 7: GET FIT, GET MOVING

Preparation/Materials
- Optional: three large cards labeled *flexibility, endurance, strength*
- Optional: music to accompany exercising and cooling down
- Student books

Objectives
- Students will identify strength, endurance, and flexibility as components of physical fitness.
- Students will recognize the benefits of physical fitness.
- Students will understand that keeping physically fit is part of our responsibility as Christians.

Background
The Canadian Association for Health, Physical Education, and Recreation (CAHPER) promotes physical fitness in the lives of all young Canadians through the QDPE program, Quality Daily Physical Education. The program uses Canada Fitness Awards and other resources to motivate and educate students.

In the United States, SHAPE America (shapeamerica.org) and the Office of Disease Prevention and Health Promotion (through health.gov) both provide resources and guidelines for children's health and fitness. Shape America provides many free downloads, schedules, and specific guidance towards promoting activity. Health.gov focuses on the specific health recommendations and links to the President's Council on Sports, Fitness, and Nutrition, which includes an incentive program as a reward for physical activity.

This lesson raises awareness of the importance of physical fitness in building a healthy lifestyle and identifies the benefits of fitness. Students learn that several types of activities are necessary to develop fitness, with different exercises developing different muscle groups and aspects of fitness. The lesson focuses on three specific components of physical fitness programs—strength, endurance, and flexibility.

The suggested exercises for flexibility and strength are taken from CSI's *Physical Education, 3–6.* You may wish to use your school's physical education teacher as a resource person for this lesson. Some of the suggested exercises call for quite a bit of space; however, each group of exercises also contains exercises that can be done in the classroom.

- -

Lesson
1. Do some exercises or activities with the class that demonstrate the three main components of physical fitness: flexibility, strength, and endurance.

   Flexibility. Begin with a two or more stretching exercises (which also serve as a warm-up) to illustrate flexibility. Direct students to stretch slowly. Hold the stretch position for at least twenty seconds. Tell students to think about the exercises as you do them and be ready to say how they benefit the body.
   - Standing stretch. Stand on toes and reach as high as possible with right arm, then with left. Recover and repeat.

- Hamstring stretch. Stand erect. Place right hand on left shoulder with elbow pointing down. Cross right foot in front of left. Bend slowly at waist and point elbow down. Keep knees straight. Repeat to opposite side.
- Spine rotation. Stand erect with arms held at shoulder height and elbows out. Twist trunk as far as possible to each side, keeping feet in place.
- Sitting stretch. Sit with legs extended forward and feet about 1 meter apart. Clasp hands behind neck and point elbows forward. Bring elbows as close as possible to tops of legs without moving legs. Repeat.

Ask the class to identify how the activity helps them. Briefly discuss the importance of *flexibility*, as you write the word on the board or hold up a card with the word on it. When we have flexibility, we can use the body easily over a full range of motion. Have students act out how they might move if their bodies were not flexible at all. (Note that stretching exercises are also used to warm up muscles before more strenuous exercise in order to prevent muscle injury or soreness.)

Strength. The following are a few strength-building exercises. These are isometric exercises that are characterized by a high degree of muscular tension and very little movement of body parts. Have students hold muscles in contracting position during a slow count to 10. Again direct students to think about how the exercises will help them.
- Biceps. With left palm up and right palm down, clasp hands in front of body, chest high. Try to bring left hand up, while resisting with right. Hold. Reverse and try to bring up right hand.
- Chest. Clasp fingers together in front of chest with forearms parallel to the floor. Pull against fingers to force elbows out. Hold.
- Chest. Stand up straight. Place left palm in right palm with forearms held parallel to the floor. Press palms together as hard as possible. Hold.
- Legs. Sit up straight. Bend one knee to chest. Hold on to bent leg by folding hands in front of shin. Try to straighten leg against pull of arms. Hold. Repeat with other leg.

Ask: "What effect do these exercises have? (Strengthening muscles). What happens when muscles aren't used? (Become weaker.) What happens to muscles when they are used and exercised? (Become stronger and bigger.) Why do people who are injured often do special exercises?" (To help the muscle recover from the injury; to bring the muscle back to normal strength). Write the word *strength* on the board or show the card with the word. Consider also having students suggest other exercises they do in physical education classes that develop strength (for example, chin-ups, pull-ups, bent knee sit-ups, squat-thrusts).

Endurance. Do one vigorous exercise as an example of aerobic activity that helps build cardiovascular fitness. Follow the same procedure of asking students to think about the effect of the exercise on the body.

- Jumping Jacks. Stand with feet together and hold your arms against your sides. Hop, spreading legs apart and swinging arms up and over the head. Hop again and at the same time bring legs together and lower arms to sides. Do these as many times as the class can without stopping.
- Skip-walk-run-walk. Take four laps around the gym or open area. On the first round, skip; on the second, walk fast; on the third, run; on the fourth, walk fast.
- Running in place. Have students jog in place until they are slightly tired and out of breath.

Ask: "Was it hard to keep on jumping without stopping? Do you think if you often did this exercise you would be able to do it for a longer period of time? How do you think this kind of exercise can help you?" (Accept all answers.) Introduce and explain the word *endurance.* Discuss how doing this type of exercise until they're out of breath can be one way to make the heart and lungs stronger. Consider having students repeat the exercise and check their pulse rate or recall with students their experience in unit 1 with monitoring pulse rates (See Unit 1, Lesson 6 for a pulse rate chart).

Optional: Play music and give students time to relax and move slowly to the music as they cool down.

2. With the three words before the students, explain that developing flexibility, strength, and endurance are all important parts of a fitness program. Have students name specific things that they do daily that help them develop one of these areas. Or, if you wish, have student pairs or work groups make up lists of these types of activities.

3. **Student book.** Read "Get Fit, Get Moving" with the class and answer the "Think It Over" questions together.

    1. *Being in good physical shape. Consider reviewing the role of nutrition in fitness and discussing the influence of physical health on mental health.*
    2. *Helps you to be safe—for example, how far and fast can you run to get help in an emergency or how long can you hold on to a tree branch if you slip during tree climbing; helps you to feel better about yourself; allows you to enjoy physically demanding activities, etc.*
    3. *Answers will vary.*
    4. *Answers will vary.*

• •

Related Activities

1. Organize an exercise club. You may wish to work with the physical education teacher on this project. Students will need help deciding on appropriate exercises/activities and on a time and place to meet. You may also wish to teach the students how to take their pulse before and after each of their exercises.

2. Have students keep a fitness log for one week, in which they list what they've done to "get moving, get fit."

3. Have each student set personal goals for fitness. Work with the physical education teacher to develop a schedule and appropriate exercises. Emphasize success and enjoyment.

4. Use print and audiovisuals to extend or reinforce the lesson. Ideas can be found through shapeamerica.org or on the resources list.

LESSON 8: STAND UP STRAIGHT!

Preparation/Materials

*   Student Visual
*   For making one spine model:
    balls of plasticine or clay for making verte-
        brae, 24 about ¾" in diameter
    balls of plasticine or clay for making discs,
        23 about ½" in diameter
    piece of elastic to string sections together
*   Make a sample of two vertebrae with a disc
    sandwiched in between.

Objectives

*   Students will learn about the function and
    structure of the spine.
*   Students will identify proper posture for
    lifting, sitting, standing, and sleeping.
*   Students will become aware of the impor-
    tance of proper posture for health.

Background

The spine is a very important part of the
wonderful body God has created. It is made of
26 bones linked together (children have more,
but some gradually fuse). The top 24 bones are
called vertebrae. The spinal cord, the body's
main nerve line, travels from the brain down a
channel through each vertebrae. Strong muscles running from the spine to the skull hold the
head up. The spine is strong and easily makes
thousands of bends and movements each day.
However, muscle fitness is essential for good
posture, and a lack of fitness can lead to lower-
back pain and back soreness in adults.

A healthy spine is not straight when viewed
from the side; sections of the spine are curved
to absorb the shock of jumping and walking.
Good posture ensures that the vertebrae can
function freely and properly.

. . . .

Lesson

1. Introduce this lesson by playing a guessing game with the class. To a student who is sit-
    ting up straight say, "You have it!" To a student who is slouching say, "I'm afraid you don't
    have it." Repeat the procedure several times and then ask class members what they
    think they have/don't have (good posture). If they don't have a clue, drop broad hints.

2. **Student visual.** Refer to the visual of the spine (also called spinal column, backbone, or
    vertebral column) in the student workbook and discuss its structure. Note that the
    spine must be rigid enough to support the head and the weight of the body, but it must
    also be flexible enough to allow us to move. How flexible is the spine? Note that we can
    actually twist the spine enough to bend over or to look behind our back. (Have some
    students try these movements.)

    Explain that the spine is made of 26 small bones ("How does this provide flexibility and
    strength?") The 24 top bones are called vertebrae. The vertebrae are separated by a
    disc, or pad, of cartilage (recall cartilage as the rubbery substance found in the nose and
    ear). Inside the spine is a thick bunch of nerves, called the spinal cord, that connects
    your brain to the rest of your body (consider referring to Unit 1, Lesson 10 drawing of

the nervous system). Strong muscles running from the spine to the skull hold up your head. Teach new vocabulary.

Students may be interested in knowing that as we walk around during the day, the weight of our upper body squashes the discs, so that we are a little shorter by evening.

3. Relate the information about how the spine is constructed to good posture. Demonstrate proper posture in lifting, sitting, and standing positions. You may also wish to slouch or sit with incorrect posture and have students identify how this affects the spine.
   - Lifting: Keep load close to the body. Bend knees and elbows, not the back.
   - Sitting: Sit straight with feet flat on the floor. The whole back needs the support of the back of the chair. Avoid slouching.
   - Standing/Walking: Stand straight (not rigidly straight).
   - Sleeping: Sleeping on the back or side places less stress on the spine.

   Have student pairs work together to review the postures just demonstrated. One student can assume the proper posture while the other traces the spine to feel the proper position.

   Elicit from students the results of poor posture. (Aches and pains in the back. If the back is mistreated over a long period of time, as a person gets older back problems develop. Because poor posture throws the body out of line, other parts of the body may be affected also. Poor posture also keeps a person from looking his or her best.)

4. Have students make models of the spine. Distribute materials and show students the sample section of the spinal column to help them visualize the project. Explain how students are to make the model.
5. Conclude by talking about the models and the function of the spine. What do the clay

---

Directions for making a model of the spine

1. Flatten each of the ¾" balls of plasticine or clay, pinch one end, and make a hole through that end with a pencil.

2. Flatten the ½" ball to make a disc.

3. Direct each student to make a selection of the spine and then team up with others to add the nerves and make a spinal column of 24 vertebrae, or have each student make an individual model of a section of the spinal column using 5 vertebrae and 4 discs and a short piece of elastic. Tie knots in the elastic on both ends. If you wish, display the models by suspending them from clothes hangers ot by tacking them to a bulletin board

---

sections and elastic represent? What's the difference between the model and the real thing? (The human spine is made of cells and has nerves; the spine grows.) Point out that a pair of nerves branches off between each bone or vertebra. Ask students why the spinal cord runs through the bone. (For protection. Stress the importance of the spinal cord; review why paralysis results if the spinal cord is broken in an accident.) Briefly summarize or elicit from students why good posture is important for health.

• •

Related Activity

- Obtain a record/cassette such as *Learning Basic Skills Through Music, Health & Safety, vol. 3* and do the section on posture exercises.

LESSON 9: WHY BUY?

Preparation/Materials
- Samples of packaged common health-related products: toothpaste, mouthwash, cotton swabs, nail-care products, soap, shampoo, tissues (If possible have one sample of toothpaste that carries an endorsement from the American Dental Association or another reliable organization.)
- Optional: some pre-recorded TV commercials for health/cosmetic products to show to the class
- Cards with ideas for imaginary products written on them

Objectives
- Students will identify common health products and will recognize the reasons for their use.
- Students will recognize labels as sources of consumer information.
- Students will become aware of advertising and its techniques.

Background
According to the British Health Education Council's *Children Need Health Care* (Conner, 1988) young children respond well to the challenge of looking after their own bodies. Teaching them to be discerning about health-care products is one aspect of body care. In Unit 5 students examined ads for over-the-counter medications, tobacco products, and alcohol, and identified their implied messages; in this lesson students consider how advertisements affect our purchase of personal health-care products.

Lesson
1. Brainstorm with the students a list of health products they commonly use. These are products that help us to feel better, smell clean, and look after our bodies. As the students give their ideas, pull out the products you have brought as examples.

2. Ask the students the following questions:
   - "How do you know how to use these products?"
   - "How much (mouthwash, etc.) do you use?"
   - "How long do you use it?"
   - "What does (name of product) do?"

   If they answer that their parents tell them, ask them how their parents know how to use the products.

   Give each pair of students a product and ask them to search for the information they would need to know in order to use that product. Allow time for the students to discover the labels/information on the packages. Discuss what the labels say. What important information is included? (For example, some toothpastes include fluoride and others don't. What would be the best brand for preventing cavities?) Are they making any promises? Is there an organization or famous person endorsing the product?

Do they tell you what to do if it doesn't work or if it works improperly (side effects)? Decide how many of these products we really need.

3. Show students the video of previously recorded TV ads to discover/review how advertising works. How does advertising influence our decision to buy? (Attractive packaging, endorsement of a famous person, making promises to provide something we want or need.) Remind students of the power of advertising techniques and of the need to be careful consumers.

4. Divide the class into pairs and provide each pair with an imaginary product card. Each card should have the name/description of an unusual product.

   Examples of imaginary products:
   - Chocolate-flavored toothpaste
   - Onion-flavored mouthwash
   - Eyeglass frames that change color to match your clothes
   - Adhesive bandages guaranteed never to come off
   - A no-rinse-off soap that is also a sun lotion
   - First-aid cream that can also be used as finger paint
   - Facial tissues made from lamb's wool
   - Deodorant/toothpaste combination package or product
   - Hair brush with five non-hair related uses
   - Shampoo product that coats hair, making once-a-month shampoos the rule
   - Toothbrush containing enough toothpaste right in the bristles (time-release) to last one week

   Have each pair make an advertisement for their product. How can they get people to buy their product?

   Have each pair present its advertisement/product to the rest of the class. Ask the other students to listen carefully to spot unrealistic promises.

   Alternative option: have students create a poster, a radio ad, or a jingle to promote their product.

5. **Summarize.** Advertisers want us to believe that we need their products. We have to use our money wisely and make good choices. Elicit from students why reading product labels is important.

Related Activity
- Create actual models of the personal health-care product as an art project.

LESSON 10: LIVING IN A HEALTHY COMMUNITY

Preparation/Materials
- Student books
- Optional: Invite a resource person from a community agency to discuss what the agency does to promote community health.

Objectives
- Students will become aware that members of a community depend on each other for maintaining a healthy community.
- Students will identify places/services in the community that help to keep the community healthy.
- Students will take responsibility to contribute to community.

Background
The health of a community is protected by government codes and laws that set standards for air and water quality, housing, food handling and storing, and other important basic services or aspects of community life. Local councils and agencies monitor and enforce compliance.

This lesson raises student consciousness of community health issues and encourages them to take their share of responsibility for the health of the community.

- -

Lesson

1. Briefly introduce the topic of community health: "Throughout the unit, we have been talking about what each person can do to keep himself or herself healthy, but in order to build a healthy lifestyle we also need to depend on many other people in our community." Tell students that in this lesson they will be thinking about how the community helps them to be healthy. Ask: "Is there such a thing as a healthy community? How can a community be healthy?" Tell students that's one question they'll be thinking about in this lesson.

2. On the board draw a simple map and have students copy the map on a piece of paper. Tell students that they are to think about places in the community that help make the community healthy. Offer or elicit one or two suggestions (hospital and drug store or pharmacy). Show students how to make a key to mark these places on the map.

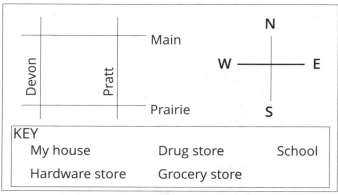

Direct students to draw in as many places as they can think of. They should be prepared to tell how the place or the people working there help to make the community a healthy place. Students can work in groups to help each other complete the maps.

Then have groups share the places (or at least three places) on its community map. (Some possible suggestions: parks or gyms for places to exercise and build fitness; hospitals, clinics, doctors' offices for taking care of sick people, giving immunizations, etc.; dental offices; drug stores/pharmacies for dispensing medicines; water department to provide community with safe water; opticians to provide eyeglasses; ambulances/paramedics for emergencies; recycling center/landfill for disposal of trash.) If students have not included houses or schools or stores, ask how these things can contribute to health.

3. **Student book.** Read "Living in a Healthy Community." Discuss the health department's role in monitoring the community's water, air, and food. (Recall that people need water, oxygen, and food to live.) Then bring in the Christian perspective as you read and discuss what each individual can do to make the community a healthy place to live. Answer the "Think It Over" questions.

   1. *Include safe methods of preparing and storing foods; cleanliness of the kitchen, of food storage areas, of utensils and dishes, of workers' hands.*
   2. *People need food to live; food that is not properly stored or prepared will make people sick.*
   3. *Water is necessary for life. Unsafe water can make a whole community sick.*
   4. *People need air to live; polluted air can make people sick. You may wish to talk about smog alerts that are issued when the level of pollution is very high.*
   5. *Leave public restrooms and drinking fountains clean; follow community rules for immunizations; dispose of garbage and trash properly, etc.*
   6. *Answers will vary.*

4. Optional: Have a public-health nurse or representative of a health agency speak to the class about community health. Before the visit have the class prepare specific questions to ask.

5. Integrate with language arts and have students complete one of the following writing assignments.
   - Write stories about a community that lacks one of the places/services identified in Step 2 of the lesson. Students can describe how health problems arise in the community as a result. For example, if there is no proper garbage disposal or no check on cleanliness in food handling, what might happen?
   - Write paragraphs about the presentation of the resource person, telling what new things they learned about community health from the speaker or perhaps telling about one interesting aspect of the presentation.
   - Write a description of one thing they or their family do that contributes to community health.

Related Activities

1. Working as a whole class, write a letter to the health department to find out what kind of checks are used to monitor air pollution or to the sanitation department to find out about recycling efforts or the system of garbage disposal.

2. Volunteers may wish to research how the community maintains its swimming pool or tests the water of a nearby lake to protect the health of the public.

3. Plan a field trip to the community's water filtration plant or recycling center.

4. Assist the class to form a strategy for raising awareness of the problem of litter at school. Perhaps have them check places where litter frequently collects and decide what can be done about it.

LESSON 11: BUILDING BLOCKS FOR HEALTH

Preparation/Materials

- For the building block activity: Label large blocks with the name of an important building block of health covered in this lesson. Borrow large, cardboard blocks from a lower-level class and attach labels with masking tape, or use shoe boxes covered with construction paper.
- Drawing paper, at least one sheet for every pair of students
- Materials for culminating activities as desired
- Unit Evaluation

Objectives

- Students will review health concepts.
- Students will recognize that a healthy lifestyle has many components.
- Students will decide to build a healthy lifestyle.

● ●

Lesson

1. Review the unit with a "building blocks for healthy living" activity. Hold up a labeled block and ask students to tell how the topic/item contributes to health. Add any important points missed by students. Put the block on the table and as you add successive topics/blocks build a pyramid. All these blocks—and more—contribute to a healthy lifestyle.

   After students have seen the pyramid and reviewed topic titles, distribute the blocks to students working in pairs or trios. Tell students to keep the label or topic of their block a secret from the rest of the class. Direct students to draw a picture that reminds them of the message/lesson of their given box. After 5–10 minutes, collect the boxes (still hiding labels) and the pictures. Show the pictures to the class, one at a time. Have the class guess which "building block" is pictured as you or class members build the good health pyramid again.

2. **Unit evaluation.** Use the worksheet to review and evaluate.

   Fill in the blank:
   1. cells, 2. nutrients, 3. nutrition, 4. crown, 5. primary, 6. root, 7. plaque, 8. flexibility, 9. endurance, 10. spine.

   Short essay:
   1. Answers will vary.
   2. Answers might include brushing teeth, flossing teeth, visiting the dentist regularly, and eating healthy food.
   3. Answers will vary.
   4. Answers will vary.
   5. Compare to MyPlate in the Student Book.

3. Choose one or more of the following as culminating activities:
    *   Make up skits focusing on one or more components of a healthy lifestyle. Create characters such as Eddie Exercise, Suzie Snacker, Polly Posture, Ned Nutritionist, Corkie Clean, and present the skits to another class.
    *   Work with children to make up lyrics about healthy living to a familiar melody. Review elements of a healthy lifestyle at the same time. Use a simple melody such as "The Muffin Man," "She'll Be Comin' Round the Mountain," or "Red River Valley."
    *   Hold an in-class health fair. Each student can create a display about one of the topics covered in the unit or course. Stress that the displays should be informative.
    *   Show a film or video that covers the basics of health care as an overview of the topic. Suggested titles: *Health and Your Body*, Britannica; *Mr. Know-It-Owl's Health Tips,* Kimbo Educational; *Zardip's Quest,* TVOntario.

Male/Female Body Parts

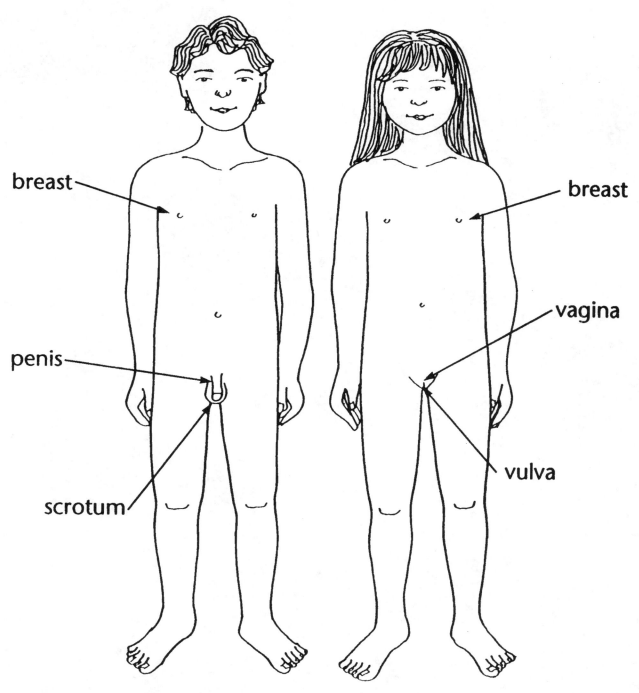

breast

breast

vagina

penis

vulva

scrotum

Private Body Parts

Permission granted to reproduce this page only.